D1082740

VECTOR ALGEBRA

P W S

THE PRINDLE, WEBER & SCHMIDT
COMPLEMENTARY SERIES IN MATHEMATICS

Under the consulting editorship of

HOWARD W. EVES

The University of Maine

TITLES IN THE SERIES:
Howard W. Eves, Functions of a Complex Variable, Volume One
Howard W. Eves, Functions of a Complex Variable, Volume Two
Edward H. Barry, Introduction to Geometrical Transformations, Volume Three
Richard E. Johnson, Vector Algebra, Volume Four

Vector Algebra

RICHARD E. JOHNSON

VOLUME FOUR

PRINDLE, WEBER & SCHMIDT, INCORPORATED

Boston, Massachusetts

53 State Street, Boston, Massachusetts

Library of Congress Catalog Card Number: 66–20380
Printed in the United States of America

Preface

Finite-dimensional vector spaces are particularly suited as the first topic for study in abstract Algebra. One reason for this is that the theory is straightforward without being trivial, and it leads to a complete description of such algebraic systems. Another reason is that vector spaces are encountered in all branches of mathematics, from analysis through geometry and topology. Finally, there are concrete examples of vector spaces available to illustrate the theory as well as to prepare the student for applications in physics, engineering, and other sciences.

Throughout the book, the underlying field of scalars is assumed to be the real number field **R**. However, in almost all sections of the book any other field F could be substituted for **R** without necessitating any changes.

The simple properties of vector spaces and their subspaces are given in the first chapter. The two principal examples of vector spaces, geometric vector spaces and the space of n-tuples of real numbers, are also presented in this chapter so that they might be used throughout the book.

Most of the theory is in Chapter 2, where the invariance of the dimension of a vector space is proved. Inner products are discussed in Chapter 3, and the existence of a normal orthogonal basis is proved for finite-dimensional vector spaces.

The very useful cross product operation in geometric vector spaces is investigated in Chapter 4. Then applications are made to the finding of equations of lines and planes in space.

In an appendix, fields in general and ordered fields in particular are defined. There is also a short section on coordinate systems for lines, planes, and space. Vector spaces over the complex number field are touched on briefly in another section. The final section relates the algebra of vectors to the quaternion algebra of Hamilton.

It is hoped that the book might prove useful in a variety of ways. In the first place, the material is detailed and amply illustrated for individual study. Thus, the student of physics or mathematics could use the book for supplementary reading on vectors. Another possible use is as a text in a senior high school course on abstract algebra. Finally, this book, along with Linear Algebra in the Prindle, Weber & Schmidt Complementary Series could serve as texts in a college course on vectors and linear algebras.

RICHARD E. JOHNSON

Contents

CHAPTER ONE. VECTOR SPACES 1

1. Definition 1
2. Subspaces 4
3. Geometric Vectors 6
4. Vector *n*-Tuples 18

CHAPTER TWO. BASES OF A VECTOR SPACE 23

1. Independence 23
2. Bases 26
3. Dimension 30
4. Homomorphisms 38

CHAPTER THREE. INNER PRODUCT SPACES 51

1. Inner Products 51
2. Normal Orthogonal Bases 63

CHAPTER FOUR. VECTOR ALGEBRAS 67

1. Two-Dimensional Algebra 67
2. Three-Dimensional Algebra 72
3. Lines in Space 80
4. Planes in Space 88

APPENDIX 95

1. Fields 95
2. Coordinate Systems 100
3. Unitary Spaces 103
4. Historical Note 106

Index 111

Chapter One

Vector Spaces

1. DEFINITION

A vector is an element of a vector space. In turn, a vector space is a set of objects, called vectors, which is closed under operations of addition and scalar multiplication and which satisfies certain algebraic laws. A precise definition of a vector space is given below.

It is worthwhile to study vector spaces for the reason that many of the algebraic systems encountered in applications of mathematics are in essence vector spaces. By studying general vector spaces, without regard to the nature of the elements, we can develop the properties common to all vector spaces.

Throughout this book the set of all real numbers will be denoted by R. There are two basic operations in R, addition and multiplication, and a basic order relation of greater than or equal to. Of course, R also has operations of subtraction and division, and order relations of greater than, less than or equal to, and less than. With respect to its operations and relations, R is an ordered field as defined in the Appendix.

1.1 DEFINITION OF A VECTOR SPACE. A vector space consists of a set V, an operation of addition in V, and an operation of scalar multiplication of V by R. Addition in V has the following properties:

(1) $\mathbf{x} + \mathbf{y} = \mathbf{y} + \mathbf{x}$ for all $\mathbf{x}, \mathbf{y} \in V$. (*Commutative law*)
(2) $\mathbf{x} + (\mathbf{y} + \mathbf{z}) = (\mathbf{x} + \mathbf{y}) + \mathbf{z}$ for all $\mathbf{x}, \mathbf{y}, \mathbf{z} \in V$. (*Associative law*)
(3) There exists an element $\mathbf{0}$ in V such that
$\mathbf{0} + \mathbf{x} = \mathbf{x} + \mathbf{0} = \mathbf{x}$ for all $\mathbf{x} \in V$. (*Identity element*)
(4) Associated with each $\mathbf{x}$ in V is an element $-\mathbf{x}$ in V such that $\mathbf{x} + (-\mathbf{x}) = (-\mathbf{x}) + \mathbf{x} = \mathbf{0}$ for all $\mathbf{x} \in V$. (*Inverse elements*)

For each $a \in \mathsf{R}$ and $\mathbf{x} \in V$, the scalar product of $\mathbf{x}$ by a is a unique element of V denoted by $a\mathbf{x}$. Scalar multiplication has the following properties:

(5) $a(\mathbf{x} + \mathbf{y}) = a\mathbf{x} + a\mathbf{y}$ for all $a \in \mathsf{R}$, $\mathbf{x}, \mathbf{y} \in V$. (*Distributive law*)
(6) $(a + b)\mathbf{x} = a\mathbf{x} + b\mathbf{x}$ for all $a, b \in \mathsf{R}$, $\mathbf{x} \in V$. (*Distributive law*)
(7) $(ab)\mathbf{x} = a(b\mathbf{x})$ for all $a, b \in \mathsf{R}$, $\mathbf{x} \in V$. (*Associative law*)
(8) $1\mathbf{x} = \mathbf{x}$ for all $\mathbf{x} \in V$. (*Identity element*)

The eight properties of addition and scalar multiplication listed above are quite familiar to all of us. Thus properties (1)–(4) are enjoyed by addition in R and properties (5)–(8) are enjoyed by multiplication in R, if we consider set V as being R.

We shall call elements of V *vectors* and those of R *scalars*. Vectors are denoted by boldface letters to clearly distinguish them from scalars. Usually, we denote scalars by the first few letters of the alphabet and vectors by the last few. In writing symbols for vectors, you might wish to put an arrow over the symbol to indicate that it denotes a vector.

Additional properties of a vector space may be derived from the eight defining ones. For example, we might expect the following properties to hold since corresponding ones hold in a field. Let V be a vector space, $\mathbf{x}, \mathbf{y}, \mathbf{z} \in V$, and $a \in \mathsf{R}$.

1.2 If $\mathbf{x} + \mathbf{z} = \mathbf{y} + \mathbf{z}$ or $\mathbf{z} + \mathbf{x} = \mathbf{z} + \mathbf{y}$, then $\mathbf{x} = \mathbf{y}$. (*Cancellation law*)

1.3 $$a\mathbf{x} = \mathbf{0} \text{ if and only if either } a = 0 \text{ or } \mathbf{x} = \mathbf{0}.$$

1.4 $$-(a\mathbf{x}) = (-a)\mathbf{x} = a(-\mathbf{x}).$$

Proof of 1.2: If $\mathbf{x} + \mathbf{z} = \mathbf{y} + \mathbf{z}$, then

$$(\mathbf{x} + \mathbf{z}) + (-\mathbf{z}) = (\mathbf{y} + \mathbf{z}) + (-\mathbf{z})$$

$$\mathbf{x} + [\mathbf{z} + (-\mathbf{z})] = \mathbf{y} + [\mathbf{z} + (-\mathbf{z})] \qquad \text{(Assoc. law)}$$

$$\mathbf{x} + \mathbf{0} = \mathbf{y} + \mathbf{0} \qquad \text{(Inverse el.)}$$

$$\mathbf{x} = \mathbf{y} \qquad \text{(Identity el.).}$$

If $\mathbf{z} + \mathbf{x} = \mathbf{z} + \mathbf{y}$, then $\mathbf{x} + \mathbf{z} = \mathbf{y} + \mathbf{z}$ by the commutative law and $\mathbf{x} = \mathbf{y}$ by the proof above.

Proof of 1.3: This property states that $a\mathbf{x} = \mathbf{0}$ if and only if a is the zero scalar or $\mathbf{x}$ is the zero vector. If $a = 0$, the zero element of R, then $0 = 0 + 0$ and $0\mathbf{x} = (0 + 0)\mathbf{x} = 0\mathbf{x} + 0\mathbf{x}$ by 1.1(6). Since $\mathbf{0} + 0\mathbf{x} = 0\mathbf{x}$ by 1.1(3), we have

$$\mathbf{0} + 0\mathbf{x} = 0\mathbf{x} + 0\mathbf{x}$$

and

$$\mathbf{0} = 0\mathbf{x}$$

by 1.2. A similar argument shows that $a\mathbf{0} = \mathbf{0}$.

Conversely, assume that $a \in \mathsf{R}$ and $\mathbf{x} \in V$ are such that $a\mathbf{x} = \mathbf{0}$. If $a \neq 0$, then a^{-1} exists and

$$\mathbf{x} = 1\mathbf{x} = (a^{-1}a)\mathbf{x} = a^{-1}(a\mathbf{x}) = a^{-1}\mathbf{0} = \mathbf{0}.$$

If $a = 0$, then $a\mathbf{x} = \mathbf{0}$ by the proof above. This proves 1.3.

Proof of 1.4: By 1.1(4), $a\mathbf{x} + [-(a\mathbf{x})] = \mathbf{0}$, whereas by 1.1(7) and 1.3, $\mathbf{0} = 0\mathbf{x} = [a + (-a)]\mathbf{x} = a\mathbf{x} + (-a)\mathbf{x}$. Therefore

$$a\mathbf{x} + [-(a\mathbf{x})] = a\mathbf{x} + (-a)\mathbf{x}$$

and

$$-(a\mathbf{x}) = (-a)\mathbf{x}$$

by the cancellation law. A similar proof shows that $-(a\mathbf{x}) = a(-\mathbf{x})$. This proves 1.4.

The operation of subtraction in V is defined as follows:

$$\mathbf{x} - \mathbf{y} = \mathbf{x} + (-\mathbf{y}) \text{ for all } \mathbf{x}, \mathbf{y} \in V.$$

It is easily shown that vector subtraction has properties similar to those of subtraction in R. For example,

$$a(\mathbf{x} - \mathbf{y}) = a\mathbf{x} - a\mathbf{y} \text{ for all } \mathbf{x}, \mathbf{y} \in V, a \in \mathsf{R},$$

$$-(\mathbf{x} - \mathbf{y}) = (-\mathbf{x}) + \mathbf{y} \text{ for all } \mathbf{x}, \mathbf{y} \in V.$$

Henceforth we shall assume that the reader is familiar with these properties.

EXERCISES

In the following exercises V is assumed to be a vector space.

1. Prove that $a\mathbf{0} = \mathbf{0}$ for all $a \in \mathsf{R}$ (part of 1.3).

2. Prove that $-(a\mathbf{x}) = a(-\mathbf{x})$ for all $a \in \mathsf{R}$ and $\mathbf{x} \in V$ (part of 1.4).
3. State and prove a cancellation law for scalar multiplication.
4. Prove that $a(\mathbf{x} - \mathbf{y}) = a\mathbf{x} - a\mathbf{y}$ for all $\mathbf{x}, \mathbf{y} \in V$, $a \in \mathsf{R}$.
5. Prove that $-(\mathbf{x} - \mathbf{y}) = (-\mathbf{x}) + \mathbf{y}$ for all $\mathbf{x}, \mathbf{y} \in V$.

2. SUBSPACES

If V is a vector space and S is a nonempty subset of V which is closed under addition and scalar multiplication (i.e., $\mathbf{x} + \mathbf{y}$ and $a\mathbf{x}$ are in S for all $\mathbf{x}, \mathbf{y} \in S$, $a \in \mathsf{R}$), then S is a vector space in its own right. Thus $\mathbf{0} \in S$ since $\mathbf{0} = 0\mathbf{x}$ for any $\mathbf{x} \in S$. If $\mathbf{x} \in S$, then $-\mathbf{x} \in S$ also, since $-\mathbf{x} = -(1\mathbf{x}) = (-1)\mathbf{x}$. It is now clear that 1.1(1)–(8) hold for S as well as V. We call S a *subspace* of V.

For each $\mathbf{x} \in V$ the set of all scalar multiples of $\mathbf{x}$ is denoted by $\mathsf{R}\mathbf{x}$,

$$\mathsf{R}\mathbf{x} = \{a\mathbf{x} \mid a \in \mathsf{R}\}.$$

Since

$$a\mathbf{x} + b\mathbf{x} = (a + b)\mathbf{x} \quad \text{and} \quad b(a\mathbf{x}) = (ba)\mathbf{x},$$

the set $\mathsf{R}\mathbf{x}$ is closed under addition and scalar multiplication and is therefore a subspace of V. The set of scalar multiples of $\mathbf{0}$ is simply $\{\mathbf{0}\}$. Thus $\{\mathbf{0}\}$ is a subspace of V; in fact, $\{\mathbf{0}\}$ is the least subspace of V in the sense that it is contained in every other subspace of V. Trivially, V is a subspace of itself according to our definition.

We call a subspace S of V *proper* if $S \neq \{\mathbf{0}\}$ and $S \neq V$. If $\mathbf{x} \in V$, $\mathbf{x} \neq \mathbf{0}$, then $\mathsf{R}\mathbf{x}$ is a minimal nonzero subspace. For if S is a proper subspace of V and $S \subset \mathsf{R}\mathbf{x}$, and if $\mathbf{y} \in S$, $\mathbf{y} \neq \mathbf{0}$, then $\mathbf{y} = a\mathbf{x}$ for some nonzero $a \in \mathsf{R}$. Hence $(ba^{-1})\mathbf{y} = (ba^{-1})a\mathbf{x} = b\mathbf{x}$ is in S for every $b \in \mathsf{R}$ and $\mathsf{R}\mathbf{x} \subset S$. It follows that $S = \mathsf{R}\mathbf{x}$. The subspace $\mathsf{R}\mathbf{x}$ is proper unless $V = \mathsf{R}\mathbf{x}$, a rather uninteresting possibility.

If S_1 and S_2 are subspaces of a vector space V, then so is their *intersection*,

$$S_1 \cap S_2 = \{\mathbf{x} \in V \mid \mathbf{x} \in S_1 \text{ and } \mathbf{x} \in S_2\}.$$

For if $\mathbf{x}$ and $\mathbf{y}$ are in both S_1 and S_2, then so are $\mathbf{x} + \mathbf{y}$ and $a\mathbf{x}$ for every $a \in \mathsf{R}$.

More generally, if $\{S_1, S_2, \cdots, S_n\}$ is any finite set of subspaces of V, then their intersection $S_1 \cap S_2 \cap \cdots \cap S_n$ also is a subspace of V. The notation

$$\bigcap_{i=1}^{n} S_i$$

is often used for this intersection. Evidently $S_1 \cap S_2 \cap \cdots \cap S_n$ is the *largest* subspace of V contained in all the subspaces $S_1, S_2, \cdots, S_n$.

Another useful way of forming a subspace from two given subspaces S_1 and S_2 of a vector space V is to take their *sum:*

$$S_1 + S_2 = \{\mathbf{x}_1 + \mathbf{x}_2 \mid \mathbf{x}_1 \in S_1, \mathbf{x}_2 \in S_2\}.$$

To show that $S_1 + S_2$ actually is a subspace of V, let $\mathbf{x}_1 + \mathbf{x}_2, \mathbf{y}_1 + \mathbf{y}_2 \in S_1 + S_2$, where $\mathbf{x}_i, \mathbf{y}_i \in S_i$, and $a \in \mathsf{R}$. Then

$$(\mathbf{x}_1 + \mathbf{x}_2) + (\mathbf{y}_1 + \mathbf{y}_2) = (\mathbf{x}_1 + \mathbf{y}_1) + (\mathbf{x}_2 + \mathbf{y}_2) \in S_1 + S_2,$$

$$a(\mathbf{x}_1 + \mathbf{x}_2) = a\mathbf{x}_1 + a\mathbf{x}_2 \in S_1 + S_2.$$

Thus $S_1 + S_2$ is a subspace of V because it is closed under addition and scalar multiplication.

We can similarly form the sum of n subspaces $S_1, S_2, \cdots, S_n$ of V:

$$S_1 + S_2 + \cdots + S_n = \{\mathbf{x}_1 + \mathbf{x}_2 + \cdots + \mathbf{x}_n \mid \mathbf{x}_i \in S_i\}.$$

The sigma notation

$$\sum_{i=1}^{n} S_i$$

is often used for this sum. Since $\mathbf{0} \in S_i$ for each i, $x_1 + \mathbf{0} + \mathbf{0} + \cdots + \mathbf{0} = \mathbf{x}_1 \in S_1 + S_2 + \cdots + S_n$ for each $\mathbf{x}_1 \in S_1$. That is, $S_1 \subset S_1 + S_2 + \cdots + S_n$. Similarly,

$$S_j \subset \sum_{i=1}^{n} S_i \text{ for } j = 1, 2, \cdots, n.$$

It should be clear that $S_1 + S_2 + \cdots + S_n$ is the *least* subspace of V containing all the subspaces $S_1, S_2, \cdots, S_n$.

If $\mathbf{x}, \mathbf{y} \in V$, then either $\mathsf{R}\mathbf{x} \cap \mathsf{R}\mathbf{y} = \{\mathbf{0}\}$ or $\mathsf{R}\mathbf{x} = \mathsf{R}\mathbf{y}$. On the other hand,

$$\mathsf{R}\mathbf{x} + \mathsf{R}\mathbf{y} = \{a\mathbf{x} + b\mathbf{y} \mid a, b \in \mathsf{R}\}.$$

More generally, for any $\mathbf{x}_1, \mathbf{x}_2, \cdots, \mathbf{x}_n \in V$,

$$\sum_{i=1}^{n} \mathsf{R}\mathbf{x}_i = \left\{\sum_{i=1}^{n} a_i\mathbf{x}_i \mid a_i \in \mathsf{R}\right\}.$$

We call $S = \sum_{i=1}^{n} \mathsf{R}\mathbf{x}_i$ the subspace of V *spanned* by the vectors $\mathbf{x}_1, \mathbf{x}_2, \cdots, \mathbf{x}_n$. Each vector of S is said to be a *linear combination* of the n vectors $\mathbf{x}_1, \mathbf{x}_2, \cdots, \mathbf{x}_n$.

EXERCISES

1. If S_1, S_2, and S_3 are proper subspaces of V such that $S_1 \cap (S_2 + S_3) = \{\mathbf{0}\}$ and $S_2 \cap S_3 = \{\mathbf{0}\}$, then prove that $S_2 \cap (S_1 + S_3) = \{\mathbf{0}\}$.
2. Let $\mathbf{x}_1$, $\mathbf{x}_2$, and $\mathbf{x}_3$ be nonzero vectors which generate a vector space V. If $\mathbf{y} \in V$, $\mathbf{y} \neq \mathbf{0}$, prove that $\mathbf{y}$ together with some two of the vectors $\mathbf{x}_1, \mathbf{x}_2, \mathbf{x}_3$ generate V.
3. Generalize Exercise 2 from 3 to n vectors.
4. If S_1 and S_2 are subspaces of V such that $S_1 \supset S_2$, then prove that $S_1 \cap (S_2 + S) = S_2 + (S_1 \cap S)$ for every subspace S of V. (This is called the *modular law*.)

3. GEOMETRIC VECTORS

For many centuries physicists have used directed line segments to represent forces, velocities, accelerations, and other entities having both magnitude and direction. We shall describe in this section the space of geometric vectors, or directed line segments, used by physicists.

Consider a Euclidean plane, denoted by E_2, made up of points and lines satisfying the postulates of Euclidean geometry. Every ordered pair (A, B) of points in E_2 determines a *segment* with endpoints A and B and a *direction* from the *initial point* A to the *terminal point* B. We call such a directed segment a *vector* in E_2, and denote it by

$$\mathbf{AB}.$$

The set of all vectors in E_2 is denoted by

$$V_2.$$

It will be convenient to have a coordinate system in E_2 (see the Appendix) so that each vector **AB** has a length denoted by

$$|\mathbf{AB}|$$

and defined to be $d(A, B)$, the distance between points A and B.

We shall consider the vectors in V_2 to be *free vectors;* i.e., two vectors **AB** and **CD** will be considered to be equal,

$$\mathbf{AB} = \mathbf{CD},$$

if and only if either $|\mathbf{AB}| = |\mathbf{CD}| = 0$ (i.e., $A = B$ and $C = D$) or $|\mathbf{AB}| = |\mathbf{CD}| \neq 0$ and **AB**, **CD** are parallel and directed in the same way (Fig. 1.1). Thus the position of each vector in the plane is immaterial; only its length and direction are important. If we wish, all vectors can be assumed to have the same initial point.

The sum of two vectors **AB** and **BC** is defined to be **AC**,

$$\mathbf{AB} + \mathbf{BC} = \mathbf{AC},$$

as shown in Fig. 1.2. If the two vectors **AB** and **AD** have the same initial point, then their sum is **AC**,

$$\mathbf{AB} + \mathbf{AD} = \mathbf{AC},$$

where **AC** is the diagonal of the parallelogram having **AB** and **AD** as two of its sides (Fig. 1.3). This is true because $\mathbf{AD} = \mathbf{BC}$.

If the points A, B, and C are collinear, then there is no parallelogram associated with the sum $\mathbf{AB} + \mathbf{BC}$. Two possible cases are shown

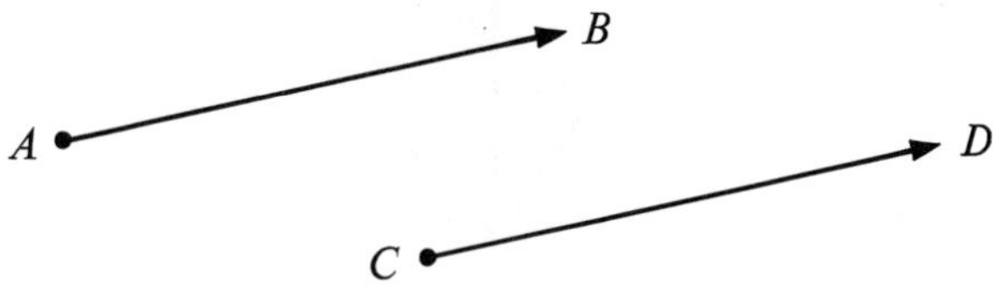

Figure 1.1

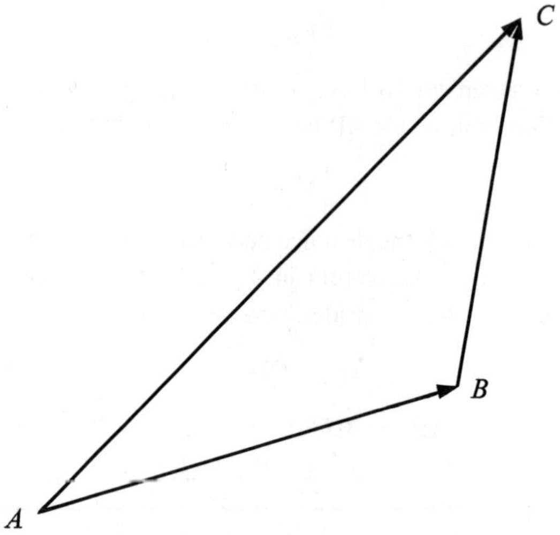

Figure 1.2

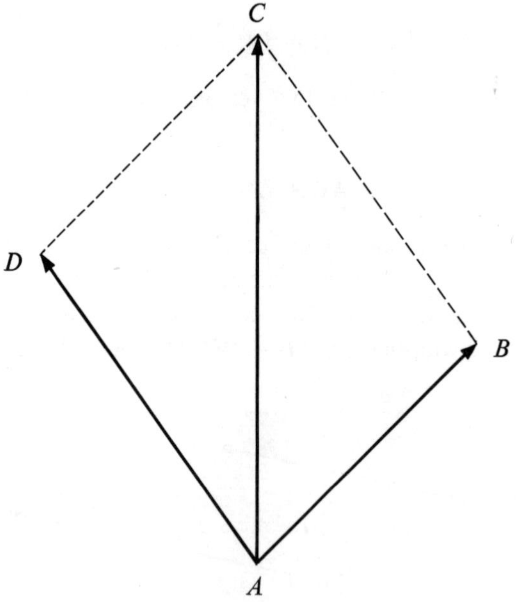

Figure 1.3

in Figs. 1.4 and 1.5.

That vector addition is commutative is illustrated in Fig. 1.6. Given vectors **AB** and **BC**, we select point D so that **AB** = **CD**. Then $ABCD$ is a parallelogram and

$$\mathbf{AB} + \mathbf{BC} = \mathbf{AC}, \quad \mathbf{BC} + \mathbf{AB} = \mathbf{BC} + \mathbf{CD} = \mathbf{BD}.$$

Since **AC** = **BD**, we have proved the *commutative law:*

1.5 $\mathbf{AB} + \mathbf{BC} = \mathbf{BC} + \mathbf{AB}$ for all $\mathbf{AB}, \mathbf{BC} \in V_2$.

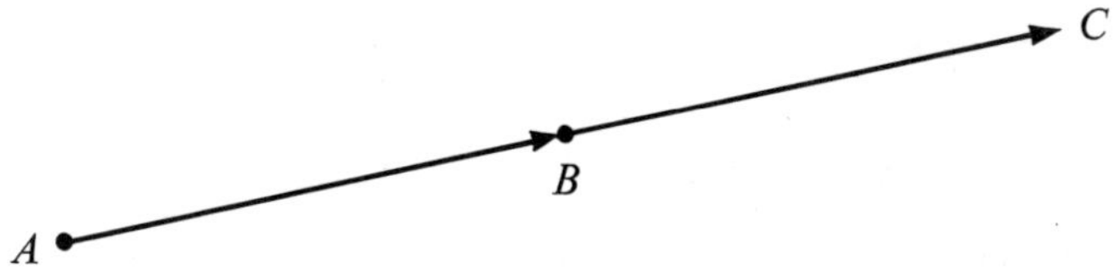

Figure 1.4

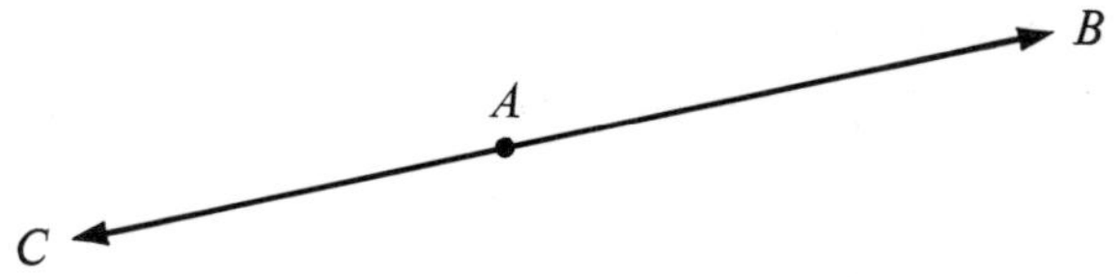

Figure 1.5

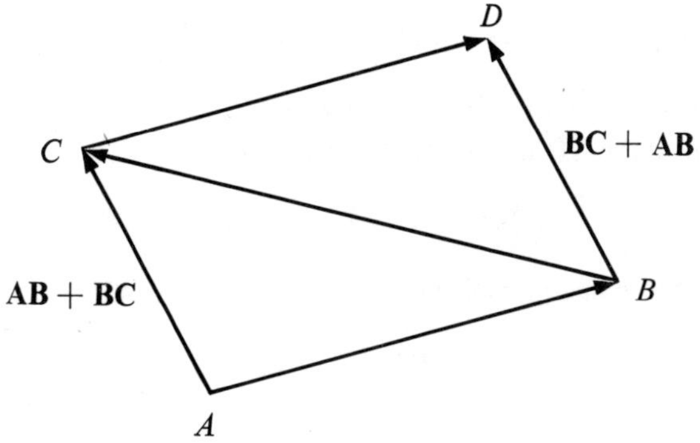

Figure 1.6

The reader should draw a new figure for the special case when A, B, and C are collinear.

Given three vectors **AB**, **BC**, and **CD**, we have

$$(\mathbf{AB} + \mathbf{BC}) + \mathbf{CD} = \mathbf{AC} + \mathbf{CD} = \mathbf{AD},$$

$$\mathbf{AB} + (\mathbf{BC} + \mathbf{CD}) = \mathbf{AB} + \mathbf{BD} = \mathbf{AD}.$$

This proves the *associative law*:

1.6 $\mathbf{AB} + (\mathbf{BC} + \mathbf{CD}) = (\mathbf{AB} + \mathbf{BC}) + \mathbf{CD}$ for all $\mathbf{AB}, \mathbf{BC}, \mathbf{CD} \in V_2$.

Given any n points $A_1, A_2, \cdots, A_n$ in E_2, evidently we have

1.7 $$\mathbf{A_1A_2} + \mathbf{A_2A_3} + \cdots + \mathbf{A_{n-1}A_n} = \mathbf{A_1A_n}.$$

We understand the sum above to be evaluated from left to right. Thus we first find $\mathbf{A_1A_2} + \mathbf{A_2A_3} = \mathbf{A_1A_3}$, next we find $\mathbf{A_1A_3} + \mathbf{A_3A_4} = \mathbf{A_1A_4}$, and so on. However, since addition is commutative and associative, it does not really matter in what order we add the terms of 1.7.

A vector having the same initial and terminal point is called the *zero vector* and is denoted by **0**. Thus

$$\mathbf{0} = \mathbf{AA}$$

for every point A in E_2. The vector **0** is not considered to have any particular direction. Clearly

1.8 $$\mathbf{AB} + \mathbf{0} = \mathbf{0} + \mathbf{AB} = \mathbf{AB} \text{ for all } \mathbf{AB} \in V_2.$$

That is, **0** is the *additive identity element* of V_2.

Each vector **AB** has an opposite **BA**, and

$$\mathbf{AB} + \mathbf{BA} = \mathbf{BA} + \mathbf{AB} = \mathbf{0}.$$

We call **BA** the *negative* of **AB** and denote it by $-\mathbf{AB}$,

$$\mathbf{BA} = -\mathbf{AB}.$$

Thus

1.9 $$\mathbf{AB} + (-\mathbf{AB}) = (-\mathbf{AB}) + \mathbf{AB} = \mathbf{0} \text{ for all } \mathbf{AB} \in V_2.$$

This proves the *additive inverse* property.

The difference of two vectors is given by

$$\mathbf{AB} - \mathbf{AC} = \mathbf{CB},$$

since

$$\mathbf{AB} = \mathbf{AC} + \mathbf{CB}.$$

Thus $\mathbf{AB} + \mathbf{AC}$ and $\mathbf{AB} - \mathbf{AC}$ are the two diagonals of the parallelogram having $\mathbf{AB}$ and $\mathbf{AC}$ as adjacent sides (Fig. 1.7).

Results 1.5, 1.6, 1.8, and 1.9 may be summarized by saying that geometric vector addition in V_2 has properties 1.1(1)–(4) of addition in a vector space. However, we cannot as yet say that V_2 is a vector space because an operation of scalar multiplication has not been defined.

We define scalar multiplication in V_2 as follows. For each vector $\mathbf{AB}$ and each $r \in \mathsf{R}$, define

$$r\mathbf{AB}$$

to be the vector whose length is $|r|\ |\mathbf{AB}|$ and whose direction is (1) the same as that of $\mathbf{AB}$ if $r > 0$, and (2) opposite to that of $\mathbf{AB}$ if $r < 0$. Also define

$$0\mathbf{AB} = \mathbf{0}.$$

In other words, if A, B, and C are collinear points, then

$$r\mathbf{AB} = \mathbf{AC}, \text{ where } |\mathbf{AC}| = |r|\ |\mathbf{AB}|,$$

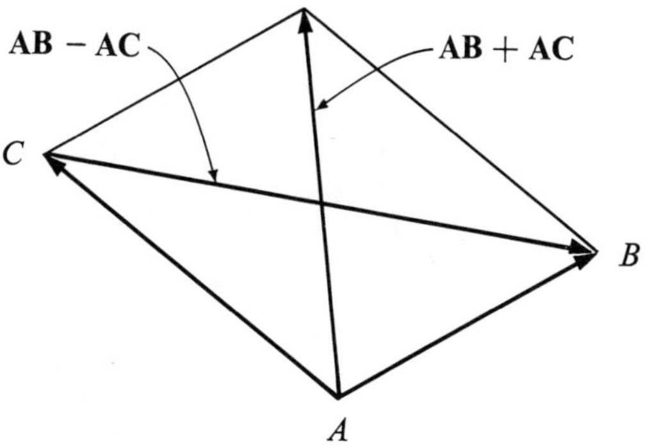

Figure 1.7

where **AB** and **AC** have the same direction if $r > 0$, and opposite directions if $r < 0$. Some examples are given in Fig. 1.8.

If **AB**, **BC** $\in V_2$ and $r \in \mathsf{R}$, then select points B' and C' so that (Fig. 1.9)

$$\mathbf{AB'} = r\mathbf{AB}, \quad \mathbf{AC'} = r\mathbf{AC}.$$

Triangles ABC and $AB'C'$ are similar by results of Euclidean geometry, so that side $B'C'$ is parallel to BC and has length $|r|$ times the length of BC. Therefore

$$\mathbf{B'C'} = r\mathbf{BC},$$

and

$$\mathbf{AB'} + \mathbf{B'C'} = r\mathbf{AB} + r\mathbf{BC} = \mathbf{AC'} = r\mathbf{AC} = r(\mathbf{AB} + \mathbf{BC}).$$

Thus we have proved

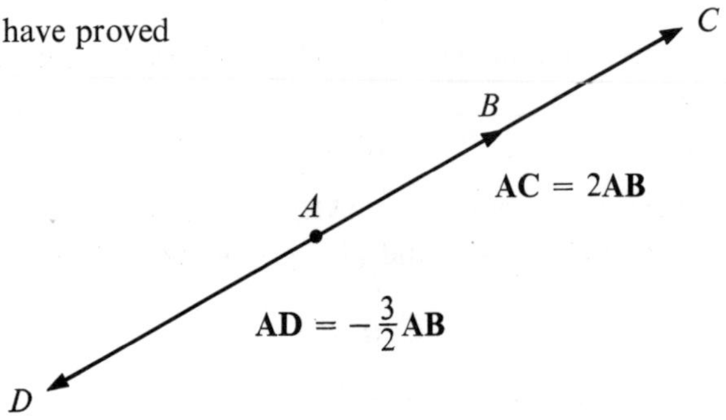

Figure 1.8

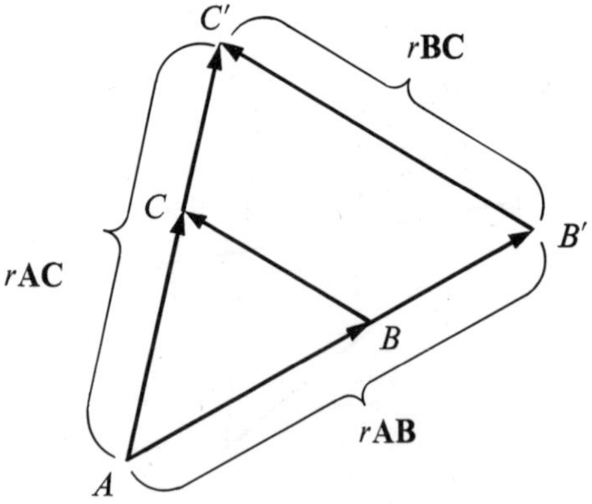

Figure 1.9

1.10 $r(\mathbf{AB} + \mathbf{BC}) = r\mathbf{AB} + r\mathbf{BC}$ for all $\mathbf{AB}, \mathbf{BC} \in V_2$, $r \in \mathsf{R}$.

If r and s are positive numbers, then the following two properties are easily shown to hold:

1.11 $(r + s)\mathbf{AB} = r\mathbf{AB} + s\mathbf{AB}$ for all $\mathbf{AB} \in V_2$, $r, s \in \mathsf{R}$.

1.12 $(rs)\mathbf{AB} = r(s\mathbf{AB})$ for all $\mathbf{AB} \in V_2$, $r, s \in \mathsf{R}$.

Thus the equation

$$|r + s|\ |\mathbf{AB}| = |r|\ |\mathbf{AB}| + |s|\ |\mathbf{AB}|$$

shows that the vectors $(r + s)\mathbf{AB}$ and $r\mathbf{AB} + s\mathbf{AB}$ have the same length, and the equation

$$|rs|\ |\mathbf{AB}| = |r|\ |s|\ |\mathbf{AB}|$$

shows that the vectors $(rs)\mathbf{AB}$ and $r(s\mathbf{AB})$ have the same length. Clearly all four vectors have the same direction as $\mathbf{AB}$. Thus 1.11 and 1.12 hold if $r > 0$ and $s > 0$. We leave to the reader the proof that they also hold if $r < 0$ or $s < 0$.

Finally, it is evident that

1.13 $1\mathbf{AB} = \mathbf{AB}$ for all $\mathbf{AB} \in V_2$.

Results 1.10–1.13 may be summarized by saying that scalar multiplication in V_2 has properties 1.1(5)–(8) of scalar multiplication in a vector space. Since we have already observed that properties 1.1(1)–(4) hold for V_2, we may state the following result.

1.14. THEOREM. V_2 is a vector space.

The fact that V_2 is a vector space may be used to solve geometric problems, as the following examples illustrate.

Example 1. Prove that the diagonals of a parallelogram bisect each other.

Solution: Let $ABCD$ be a parallelogram and let E be the midpoint of diagonal AC (Fig. 1.10). Since the opposite sides of $ABCD$ are parallel and equal,

$$\mathbf{AB} = \mathbf{DC}.$$

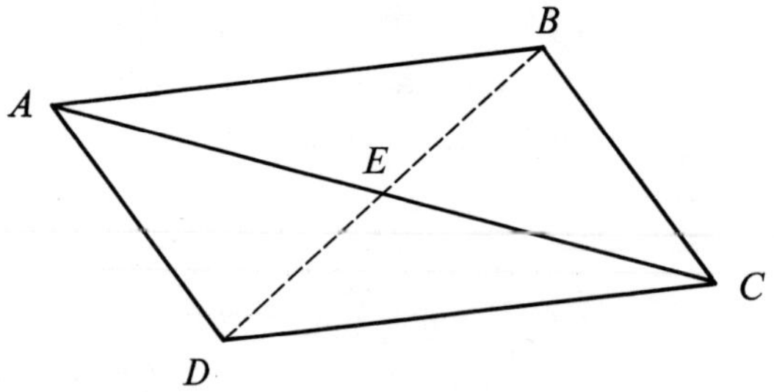

Figure 1.10

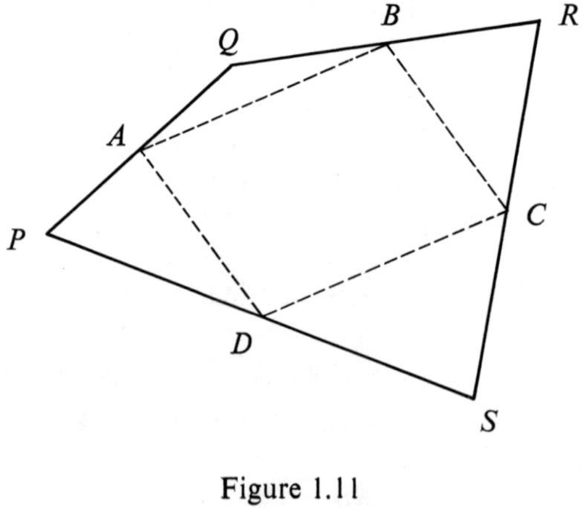

Figure 1.11

Now $\mathbf{AB} = \mathbf{AE} + \mathbf{EB}$, $\mathbf{DC} = \mathbf{DE} + \mathbf{EC}$, and $\mathbf{AE} = \mathbf{EC}$. Hence

$$\mathbf{AE} + \mathbf{EB} = \mathbf{AE} + \mathbf{DE}$$

and

$$\mathbf{EB} = \mathbf{DE}$$

by the cancellation law. Therefore B, E, and D are collinear and E is the midpoint of **DB**. Thus the diagonals bisect each other.

Example 2. Prove that the quadrilateral formed by joining the midpoints of the sides of a quadrilateral in order is a parallelogram.

Solution: Looking at Fig. 1.11, we see that

$$\mathbf{AQ} = \tfrac{1}{2}\mathbf{PQ}, \quad \mathbf{QB} = \tfrac{1}{2}\mathbf{QR},$$

and therefore

$$\begin{aligned}\mathbf{AB} = \mathbf{AQ} + \mathbf{QB} &= \tfrac{1}{2}\mathbf{PQ} + \tfrac{1}{2}\mathbf{QR} \\ &= \tfrac{1}{2}(\mathbf{PQ} + \mathbf{QR}) = \tfrac{1}{2}\mathbf{PR}.\end{aligned}$$

Similarly,

$$\mathbf{DS} = \tfrac{1}{2}\mathbf{PS}, \quad \mathbf{SC} = \tfrac{1}{2}\mathbf{SR}$$

and

$$\mathbf{DC} = \tfrac{1}{2}(\mathbf{PS} + \mathbf{SR}) = \tfrac{1}{2}\mathbf{PR}.$$

Consequently,

$$\mathbf{AB} = \mathbf{DC}$$

and $ABCD$ is a parallelogram.

Everything we did above in the Euclidean plane E_2 can also be done in Euclidean space E_3. If we let V_3 be the set of all vectors in E_3, then properties 1.5–1.13 hold in V_3 for the same reasons they hold in V_2. Therefore we can conclude that:

1.15. THEOREM. V_3 is a vector space.

It is easily verified that Example 2 holds even if the points P, Q, R, and S are not coplanar (i.e., not in a plane). The proof is the same, with each vector now taken to be in V_3 rather than V_2. Algebraic properties of V_2 and V_3 are the same; i.e., they are the properties of any vector space. However, we shall distinguish between these vector spaces after we introduce the dimension of a vector space in the next chapter.

If $\mathbf{x}$ is a nonzero vector in either V_2 or V_3, then the subspace $\mathsf{R}\mathbf{x}$ is a *line*; i.e., $\mathsf{R}\mathbf{x}$ is the set of all vectors along a line L of E_2 or E_3 (Fig. 1.12). Recalling that the vectors of V_2 and V_3 are free, we see that $\mathsf{R}\mathbf{x}$ actually consists of L and all lines parallel to L.

If $\mathbf{x}$ and $\mathbf{y}$ are nonzero and nonparallel vectors of V_2 or V_3, then $\mathsf{R}\mathbf{x}$ and $\mathsf{R}\mathbf{y}$ are as shown in Fig. 1.13. Since $\mathbf{x}$ and $\mathbf{y}$ are free vectors, we can select them to have the same initial point. That is, lines K and L of Fig. 1.13 intersect in one point. This shows geometrically that $\mathsf{R}\mathbf{x} \cap \mathsf{R}\mathbf{y} = \{\mathbf{0}\}$. Lines K and L determine a plane p. Each vector $\mathbf{z}$ in p is the diagonal of a parallelogram having two sides on K and L, as shown in Fig. 1.13, and therefore

$$\mathbf{z} = a\mathbf{x} + b\mathbf{y} \text{ for some } a, b \in \mathsf{R}.$$

Conversely, each vector of the form $a\mathbf{x} + b\mathbf{y}$ for some $a, b \in \mathsf{R}$ is in plane p. Therefore the subspace

$$\mathsf{R}\mathbf{x} + \mathsf{R}\mathbf{y}$$

consists of all vectors in plane p. If $\mathbf{x}, \mathbf{y} \in V_2$, then p must be the whole space E_2; i.e., $\mathsf{R}\mathbf{x} + \mathsf{R}\mathbf{y} = V_2$. If $\mathbf{x}, \mathbf{y} \in V_3$, then $\mathsf{R}\mathbf{x} + \mathsf{R}\mathbf{y}$ is a proper subspace of V_3.

EXERCISES

1. Prove vectorially that if the diagonals of a quadrilateral in E_2 bisect each other, then the quadrilateral is a parallelogram.
2. If $\mathbf{AD}$ is the median drawn from A in a triangle ABC, then prove that $\mathbf{AD}$ is the arithmetic average of $\mathbf{AB}$ and $\mathbf{AC}$ [i.e., $\mathbf{AD} = \frac{1}{2}(\mathbf{AB} + \mathbf{AC})$].
3. Prove vectorially that the segments joining the midpoints of opposite sides of any quadrilateral in E_3 bisect each other.
4. Prove vectorially that the midpoints of two opposite sides of a quadrilateral in E_3 together with the midpoints of the two diagonals are either collinear or the vertices of a parallelogram.
5. If $ABCD$ is a parallelogram in E_2 and P is the midpoint of side BC, then prove vectorially that the segments AP and BD meet in a point of trisection of both.

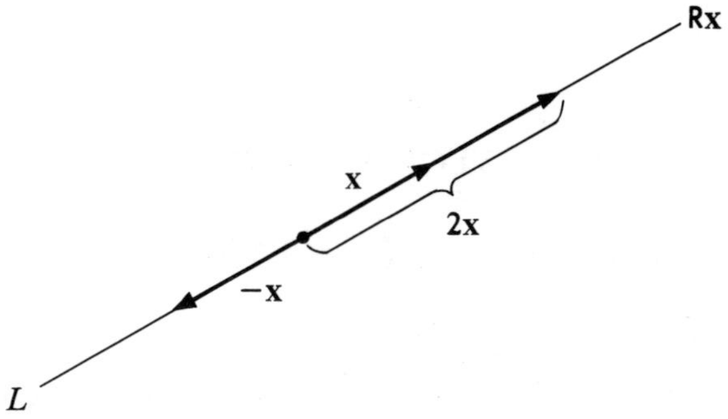

Figure 1.12

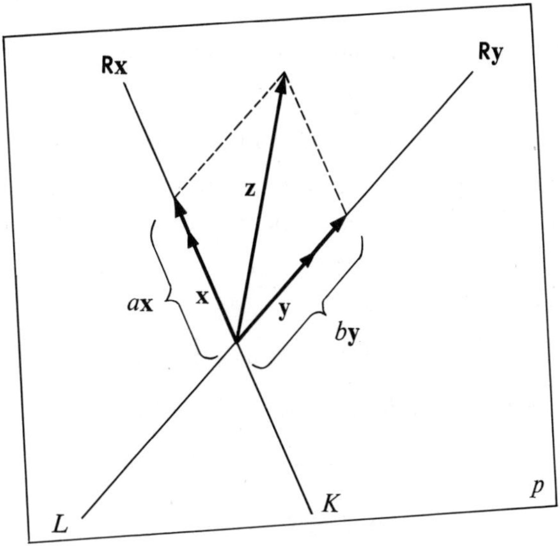

Figure 1.13

6. Exercise 5 may be generalized by assuming P is chosen on side BC so that $\mathbf{BP} = a\mathbf{BC}$, where $0 < a \leq 1$. Show vectorially that the point of intersection of AP and BD divides both segments in the same ratio, and find this ratio.

4. VECTOR n-TUPLES

Let n be a positive integer. An ordered set

$$(a_1, a_2, \cdots, a_n)$$

of n real numbers is called an *n-tuple* of real numbers. The real numbers $a_1, a_2, \cdots, a_n$ are called the *coordinates* of the n-tuple. Two n-tuples are equal if and only if they have the same coordinates:

$(a_1, a_2, \cdots, a_n) = (b_1, b_2, \cdots, b_n)$ if and only if $a_1 = b_1$, $a_2 = b_2, \cdots$, $a_n = b_n$.

We shall denote the set of all n-tuples of real numbers by

$$\mathsf{R}_n.$$

An operation of addition may be defined in R_n coordinatewise as follows:

$$(a_1, a_2, \cdots, a_n) + (b_1, b_2, \cdots, b_n) = (a_1 + b_1, a_2 + b_2, \cdots, a_n + b_n).$$

By direct computation we easily verify that properties 1.1(1)–(4) hold. Thus if $\mathbf{x} = (a_1, a_2, \cdots, a_n)$, $\mathbf{y} = (b_1, b_2, \cdots, b_n)$, and $\mathbf{z} = (c_1, c_2, \cdots, c_n)$, then

$$\mathbf{x} + (\mathbf{y} + \mathbf{z}) = (\mathbf{x} + \mathbf{y}) + \mathbf{z}$$
$$= (a_1 + b_1 + c_1, a_2 + b_2 + c_2, \cdots, a_n + b_n + c_n),$$
$$\mathbf{x} + \mathbf{y} = \mathbf{y} + \mathbf{x} = (a_1 + b_1, a_2 + b_2, \cdots, a_n + b_n)$$
$$= (b_1 + a_1, b_2 + a_2, \cdots, b_n + a_n).$$

Also, if

$$\mathbf{0} = (0, 0, \cdots, 0),$$

then

$$\mathbf{x} + \mathbf{0} = \mathbf{0} + \mathbf{x} = \mathbf{x},$$

and if

$$-\mathbf{x} = (-a_1, -a_2, \cdots, -a_n)$$

then

$$\mathbf{x} + (-\mathbf{x}) = (-\mathbf{x}) + \mathbf{x} = (0, 0, \cdots, 0) = \mathbf{0}.$$

Scalar multiplication may be defined in R_n coordinatewise as follows:

$$r(a_1, a_2, \cdots, a_n) = (ra_1, ra_2, \cdots, ra_n).$$

We verify that properties 1.1(5)–(8) hold for scalar multiplication in R_n as follows. If r, s are in R and if $\mathbf{x} = (a_1, a_2, \cdots, a_n)$, $\mathbf{y} = (b_1, b_2, \cdots, b_n)$ are in R_n, then

$$r(\mathbf{x} + \mathbf{y}) = r\mathbf{x} + r\mathbf{y} = (ra_1 + rb_1, ra_2 + rb_2, \cdots, ra_n + rb_n),$$

$$(r + s)\mathbf{x} = r\mathbf{x} + s\mathbf{x} = (ra_1 + sa_1, ra_2 + sa_2, \cdots, ra_n + sa_n),$$

$$(rs)\mathbf{x} = r(s\mathbf{x}) = (rsa_1, rsa_2, \cdots, rsa_n),$$

$$1\mathbf{x} = \mathbf{x} = (1\cdot a_1, 1\cdot a_2, \cdots, 1\cdot a_n).$$

Hence we conclude that:

1.16. THEOREM. R_n is a vector space for every positive integer n.

The vectors which have $n - 1$ coordinates 0 and the other coordinate 1 are of special significance in R_n. Let

$$\mathbf{u}_1 = (1, 0, 0, \cdots, 0, 0)$$

$$\mathbf{u}_2 = (0, 1, 0, \cdots, 0, 0)$$

$$\vdots$$

$$\mathbf{u}_n = (0, 0, 0, \cdots, 0, 1).$$

denote these vectors. Then for any $a_1, a_2, \cdots, a_n \in \mathsf{R}$,

$$a_1\mathbf{u}_1 = (a_1, 0, 0, \cdots, 0, 0)$$

$$a_2\mathbf{u}_2 = (0, a_2, 0, \cdots, 0, 0)$$

$$\vdots$$

$$a_n\mathbf{u}_n = (0, 0, 0, \cdots, 0, a_n)$$

and

$$\sum_{i=1}^{n} a_i\mathbf{u}_i = (a_1, a_2, \cdots, a_n).$$

Thus every vector $(a_1, a_2, \cdots, a_n) \in \mathsf{R}_n$ is a linear combination of the vectors $\mathbf{u}_1, \mathbf{u}_2, \cdots, \mathbf{u}_n$:

1.17 $$\mathsf{R}\mathbf{u}_1 + \mathsf{R}\mathbf{u}_2 + \cdots + \mathsf{R}\mathbf{u}_n = \mathsf{R}_n.$$

It is more difficult to decide if vectors other than the $\mathbf{u}_i$'s span R_n, as the following example shows.

Example 1. Do the vectors

$$\mathbf{x}_1 = (-1, 2, 0), \quad \mathbf{x}_2 = (3, 1, -1), \quad \mathbf{x}_3 = (1, 0, -1)$$

span R_3?

Solution: Let S be the subspace of R_3 spanned by $\mathbf{x}_1$, $\mathbf{x}_2$, and $\mathbf{x}_3$:

$$S = \mathsf{R}\mathbf{x}_1 + \mathsf{R}\mathbf{x}_2 + \mathsf{R}\mathbf{x}_3.$$

If we can show that $\mathbf{u}_1, \mathbf{u}_2, \mathbf{u}_3 \in S$, then it will follow that $\mathsf{R}\mathbf{u}_1 + \mathsf{R}\mathbf{u}_2 + \mathsf{R}\mathbf{u}_3 \subset S$ and $S = \mathsf{R}_3$ by 1.17. A possible way of doing this is as follows. Let

$$\mathbf{y}_1 = 3\mathbf{x}_1 + \mathbf{x}_2 = (0, 7, -1),$$

$$\mathbf{y}_2 = \mathbf{x}_1 + \mathbf{x}_3 = (0, 2, -1).$$

Then $\mathbf{y}_1, \mathbf{y}_2 \in S$, and hence $\mathbf{y}_3 \in S$, where

$$\mathbf{y}_3 = 2\mathbf{y}_1 - 7\mathbf{y}_2 = (0, 0, 5).$$

Therefore $\mathbf{u}_3 = \frac{1}{5}\mathbf{y}_3 \in S$. In turn, $\mathbf{y}_2 + \mathbf{u}_3 = (0, 2, 0) \in S$ and $\frac{1}{2}(\mathbf{y}_2 + \mathbf{u}_3) = \mathbf{u}_2 \in S$. Finally, $-\mathbf{x}_1 + 2\mathbf{u}_2 = \mathbf{u}_1 \in S$. We conclude that $S = \mathsf{R}_3$.

Example 2. Do the vectors

$$\mathbf{x}_1 = (2, -2, 3), \quad \mathbf{x}_2 = (3, -1, -5), \quad \mathbf{x}_3 = (-1, -5, 27)$$

span R_3?

Solution: Proceeding as in Example 1, we have

$$\mathbf{y}_1 = 3\mathbf{x}_1 - 2\mathbf{x}_2 = (0, -4, 19),$$

$$\mathbf{y}_2 = \mathbf{x}_1 + 2\mathbf{x}_3 = (0, -12, 57),$$

and hence $\mathbf{y}_1, \mathbf{y}_2 \in S = \mathsf{R}\mathbf{x}_1 + \mathsf{R}\mathbf{x}_2 + \mathsf{R}\mathbf{x}_3$. Unfortunately, $3\mathbf{y}_1 = \mathbf{y}_2$, so that we cannot conclude that $\mathbf{u}_3 \in S$ as we did in Example 1. We suspect that $\mathbf{u}_3 \notin S$. For if $\mathbf{u}_3 \in S$, then

$$a\mathbf{x}_1 + b\mathbf{x}_2 + c\mathbf{x}_3 = \mathbf{u}_3 \text{ for some } a, b, c \in \mathsf{R}.$$

That is,

$$(2a, -2a, 3a) + (3b, -b, -5b) + (-c, -5c, 27c) = (0, 0, 1)$$

and

$$\text{(1)} \qquad \begin{cases} 2a + 3b - c = 0 \\ -2a - b - 5c = 0 \\ 3a - 5b + 27c = 1. \end{cases}$$

Adding the first two equations of (1), we get

$$2b - 6c = 0, \quad \text{or} \quad b = 3c.$$

Adding -3 times the first equation of (1) to 2 times the third equation, we get

$$-19b + 57c = 2, \quad \text{or} \quad b = 3c - 2/19.$$

Since b cannot be both $3c$ and $3c - 2/19$, evidently system (1) has no solution. Therefore $\mathbf{u}_3 \notin S$, as we suspected. Consequently, the vectors $\mathbf{x}_1$, $\mathbf{x}_2$, and $\mathbf{x}_3$ do not span R_3.

EXERCISES

In each of Exercises 1–4 tell whether or not the vectors $\mathbf{x}_1$, $\mathbf{x}_2$, and $\mathbf{x}_3$ span R_3.

1. $\mathbf{x}_1 = (1, 0, 0)$, $\mathbf{x}_2 = (1, 1, 0)$, $\mathbf{x}_3 = (1, 1, 1)$.

2. $\mathbf{x}_1 = (1, 0, -1)$, $\mathbf{x}_2 = (-1, 1, 0)$, $\mathbf{x}_3 = (1, 1, -2)$.
3. $\mathbf{x}_1 = (0, 1, 2)$, $\mathbf{x}_2 = (2, 0, 1)$, $\mathbf{x}_3 = (1, 2, 0)$.
4. $\mathbf{x}_1 = (1, 0, 0)$, $\mathbf{x}_2 = (0, 1, 0)$, $\mathbf{x}_3 = (1, -1, 0)$.
5. Find two proper subspaces S_1 and S_2 of R_3 such that $S_1 \cap S_2 = \{\mathbf{0}\}$ and $S_1 + S_2 = \mathsf{R}_3$. Do the same for R_4.
6. Let $\mathbf{v}_1 = a_{11}\mathbf{u}_1$, $\mathbf{v}_2 = a_{21}\mathbf{u}_1 + a_{22}\mathbf{u}_2, \cdots, \mathbf{v}_n = a_{n1}\mathbf{u}_1 + a_{n2}\mathbf{u}_2 + \cdots + a_{nn}\mathbf{u}_n$ for some $a_{ij} \in \mathsf{R}$, with $a_{11} \neq 0, a_{22} \neq 0, \cdots, a_{nn} \neq 0$. Prove that the vectors $\mathbf{v}_1, \mathbf{v}_2, \cdots, \mathbf{v}_n$ span R_n.

Chapter Two

Bases of a Vector Space

1. INDEPENDENCE

Subspaces S_1 and S_2 of a vector space V are said to be independent if they are proper subspaces and if $S_1 \cap S_2 = \{\mathbf{0}\}$. For example, $\mathsf{R}\mathbf{x}$ and $\mathsf{R}\mathbf{y}$ are independent subspaces of V_3 if $\mathbf{x} \neq \mathbf{0}$, $\mathbf{y} \neq \mathbf{0}$, and the vectors $\mathbf{x}$ and $\mathbf{y}$ are nonparallel, i.e., $\mathsf{R}\mathbf{x} \cap \mathsf{R}\mathbf{y} = \{\mathbf{0}\}$. More generally, n subspaces of V are independent if all are proper and the intersection of any one of them with the sum of the remaining subspaces is $\{\mathbf{0}\}$, as stated below.

2.1. DEFINITION OF INDEPENDENCE. A set $\{S_1, S_2, \cdots, S_n\}$ of subspaces of a vector space V is called *independent*, and we write

$$\{S_1, S_2, \cdots, S_n\}^{\perp},$$

if and only if all $S_i \neq \{\mathbf{0}\}$ and

$$S_i \cap (S_1 + \cdots + S_{i-1} + S_{i+1} + \cdots + S_n) = \{\mathbf{0}\}, \qquad i = 1, 2, \cdots, n.$$

A nonindependent set of subspaces is called a *dependent* set. Thus if $\{T_1, T_2, \cdots, T_n\}$ is a dependent set, either some $T_i = \{\mathbf{0}\}$ or $T_i \cap (T_1 + \cdots + T_{i-1} + T_{i+1} + \cdots + T_n) \neq \{\mathbf{0}\}$ for some i.

One way of establishing that a set of subspaces is independent is as follows.

2.2. THEOREM. Let $\{S_1, S_2, \cdots, S_n\}$ be a set of nonzero subspaces of a vector space V and let $S = S_1 + S_2 + \cdots + S_n$. Then $\{S_1, S_2, \cdots, S_n\}^{\perp}$ if and only if every $\mathbf{x} \in S$ has a unique representation of the form

$$\mathbf{x} = \mathbf{x}_1 + \mathbf{x}_2 + \cdots + \mathbf{x}_n, \text{ for some } \mathbf{x}_i \in S_i.$$

Proof: If some $\mathbf{x} \in S$ has two different representations, say

$$\mathbf{x} = \mathbf{x}_1 + \mathbf{x}_2 + \cdots + \mathbf{x}_n = \mathbf{y}_1 + \mathbf{y}_2 + \cdots + \mathbf{y}_n,$$

where $\mathbf{x}_i, \mathbf{y}_i \in S_i$ and some $\mathbf{x}_i \neq \mathbf{y}_i$, say for simplicity $\mathbf{x}_1 \neq \mathbf{y}_1$, then

$$\mathbf{x}_1 - \mathbf{y}_1 = (\mathbf{y}_2 - \mathbf{x}_2) + (\mathbf{y}_3 - \mathbf{x}_3) + \cdots + (\mathbf{y}_n - \mathbf{x}_n).$$

Now $\mathbf{x}_1 - \mathbf{y}_1 \in S_1$, whereas $(\mathbf{y}_2 - \mathbf{x}_2) + (\mathbf{y}_3 - \mathbf{x}_3) + \cdots + (\mathbf{y}_n - \mathbf{x}_n) \in S_2 + S_3 + \cdots + S_n$. Thus $\mathbf{x}_1 - \mathbf{y}_1 \in S_1 \cap (S_2 + S_3 + \cdots + S_n)$ and, since $\mathbf{x}_1 - \mathbf{y}_1 \neq \mathbf{0}$, $S_1 \cap (S_2 + S_3 + \cdots + S_n) \neq \{\mathbf{0}\}$. We conclude that the set $\{S_1, S_2, \cdots, S_n\}$ is dependent.

Conversely, if $S_1 \cap (S_2 + S_3 + \cdots + S_n) \neq \{\mathbf{0}\}$, then

$$\mathbf{x}_1 = \mathbf{x}_2 + \mathbf{x}_3 + \cdots + \mathbf{x}_n \neq \mathbf{0}$$

for some $\mathbf{x}_i \in S_i$. Therefore

$$\mathbf{0} = (-\mathbf{x}_1) + \mathbf{x}_2 + \cdots + \mathbf{x}_n,$$

$$\mathbf{0} = \mathbf{0} + \mathbf{0} + \cdots + \mathbf{0}$$

are two different representations of the vector $\mathbf{0}$ as a sum of elements from the S_i. A similar argument can be made if

$$S_i \cap (S_1 + \cdots + S_{i-1} + S_{i+1} + \cdots + S_n) \neq \{\mathbf{0}\}$$

for $i \neq 1$. This proves 2.2.

Example 1. Let $S_1 = \mathsf{R}(1, -1, 2) + \mathsf{R}(2, 1, 3)$ and let $S_2 = \mathsf{R}(1, 0, -1)$ be subspaces of R_3. Is $\{S_1, S_2\}^\perp$?

Solution: Since $S_1 \neq \{\mathbf{0}\}$ and $S_2 \neq \{\mathbf{0}\}$, we need only find out if $S_1 \cap S_2 = \{\mathbf{0}\}$. We can accomplish this by looking for $a, b, c \in \mathsf{R}$ such that

$$a(1, -1, 2) + b(2, 1, 3) = c(1, 0, -1).$$

Looking at each coordinate, we see that a, b, and c must be solutions of the system of equations

$$\begin{cases} a + 2b = c \\ -a + b = 0 \\ 2a + 3b = -c. \end{cases}$$

From the second equation, $a = b$. Hence $3b = c$ from the first equation and $5b = -c$ from the third. Adding, we get $8b = 0$ and therefore $b = 0$, $a = 0$, and $c = 0$. We conclude that $S_1 \cap S_2 = \{\mathbf{0}\}$ and hence that $\{S_1, S_2\}^\perp$.

Example 2. Let $S_1 = \mathsf{R}(2, -1, 0)$, $S_2 = \mathsf{R}(3, 1, -1)$, and $S_3 = \mathsf{R}(1, -8, 3)$. Is $\{S_1, S_2, S_3\}^\perp$ in R_3?

Solution: To find out if $S_1 \cap (S_2 + S_3) = \{\mathbf{0}\}$, we solve the equation

$$a(2, -1, 0) = b(3, 1, -1) + c(1, -8, 3),$$

or the equivalent system of equations

$$\begin{cases} 2a = 3b + c \\ -a = b - 8c \\ 0 = -b + 3c. \end{cases}$$

We easily show that $a = 5c$ and $b = 3c$ is a solution for any c. Therefore $S_1 \cap (S_2 + S_3) \neq \{\mathbf{0}\}$ and the set $\{S_1, S_2, S_3\}$ is dependent.

EXERCISES

In Exercises 1–6 which of the sets of subspaces of R_3 are independent?

1. $\{S_1, S_2\}$, where $S_1 = \mathsf{R}(1, 0, 0)$ and $S_2 = \mathsf{R}(1, 1, 0)$.
2. $\{S_1, S_2\}$, where $S_1 = \mathsf{R}(1, -1, 0)$ and $S_2 = \mathsf{R}(2, 1, 1) + \mathsf{R}(1, 2, 1)$.
3. $\{S_1, S_2\}$, where $S_1 = \mathsf{R}(1, 0, 1) + \mathsf{R}(-1, 1, 0)$ and $S_2 = \mathsf{R}(1, 0, 0) + \mathsf{R}(0, 1, -1)$.
4. $\{S_1, S_2, S_3\}$, where $S_1 = \mathsf{R}(1, 0, 1)$, $S_2 = \mathsf{R}(0, 1, 0)$, and $S_3 = \mathsf{R}(0, 1, 1)$.
5. $\{S_1, S_2, S_3\}$, where $S_1 = \mathsf{R}(2, 1, 2)$, $S_2 = \mathsf{R}(-1, 5, 3)$, and $S_3 = \mathsf{R}(7, -2, 3)$.
6. $\{S_1, S_2, S_3\}$, where $S_1 = \mathsf{R}(1, -1, 5)$, $S_2 = \mathsf{R}(3, 4, -7)$, and $S_3 = \mathsf{R}(1, 2, 5)$.
7. If $\{S_1, S_2, \cdots, S_n\}^\perp$, then prove that every subset of
$$\{S_1, S_2, \cdots, S_n\}$$
is also independent.

8. If some subset of $\{S_1, S_2, \cdots, S_n\}$ is dependent, then prove that $\{S_1, S_2, \cdots, S_n\}$ is also dependent.
9. If the vector space V is spanned by the n vectors $\mathbf{x}_1, \mathbf{x}_2, \cdots, \mathbf{x}_n$ and if $\{R\mathbf{x}_1, R\mathbf{x}_2, \cdots, R\mathbf{x}_n\}$ is a dependent set, then prove that V is spanned by some $n - 1$ of the vectors $\mathbf{x}_1, \mathbf{x}_2, \cdots, \mathbf{x}_n$.
10. If $\{S_1, S_2, \cdots, S_n\}^\perp$ and S is a subspace of V such that $S \neq \{\mathbf{0}\}$ and $S \cap (S_1 + S_2 + \cdots + S_n) = \{\mathbf{0}\}$, then prove that

$$\{S, S_1, S_2, \cdots, S_n\}^\perp.$$

2. BASES

If $\mathbf{x}_1, \mathbf{x}_2, \cdots, \mathbf{x}_n$ are vectors of a vector space V, it is convenient to write

$$\{\mathbf{x}_1, \mathbf{x}_2, \cdots, \mathbf{x}_n\}^\perp \quad \text{in place of} \quad \{R\mathbf{x}_1, R\mathbf{x}_2, \cdots, R\mathbf{x}_n\}^\perp$$

and to call the vectors $\mathbf{x}_1, \mathbf{x}_2, \cdots, \mathbf{x}_n$ *linearly independent*. Of course, if $\{R\mathbf{x}_1, R\mathbf{x}_2, \cdots, R\mathbf{x}_n\}$ is a dependent set of subspaces, then we call the vectors *linearly dependent*. The following result is an easy consequence of 2.2.

2.3 THEOREM. The vectors $\mathbf{x}_1, \mathbf{x}_2, \cdots, \mathbf{x}_n$ of V are linearly independent if and only if the only solution of the equation

$$\sum_{i=1}^{n} a_i \mathbf{x}_i = \mathbf{0} \tag{1}$$

is $a_1 = 0, a_2 = 0, \cdots, a_n = 0$.

Proof: If $\{\mathbf{x}_1, \mathbf{x}_2, \cdots, \mathbf{x}_n\}^\perp$ and S is the subspace of V spanned by $\mathbf{x}_1, \mathbf{x}_2, \cdots, x_n$, then $\mathbf{0} \in S$ has the unique representation

$$\mathbf{0} = 0\mathbf{x}_1 + 0\mathbf{x}_2 + \cdots + 0\mathbf{x}_n$$

by 2.2. Hence $a_1 = 0, a_2 = 0, \cdots, a_n = 0$ is the only solution of (1). Conversely, assume that the only solution of (1) is $a_1 = 0, a_2 = 0, \cdots, a_n = 0$. If $\mathbf{x} \in S$ has representations

$$\mathbf{x} = b_1\mathbf{x}_1 + b_2\mathbf{x}_2 + \cdots + b_n\mathbf{x}_n = c_1\mathbf{x}_1 + c_2\mathbf{x}_2 + \cdots + c_n\mathbf{x}_n,$$

then

$$\mathbf{0} = (b_1 - c_1)\mathbf{x}_1 + (b_2 - c_2)\mathbf{x}_2 + \cdots + (b_n - c_n)\mathbf{x}_n.$$

Hence $b_1 - c_1 = 0, b_2 - c_2 = 0, \cdots, b_n - c_n = 0$ and $b_1 = c_1, b_2 = c_2, \cdots, b_n = c_n$. It follows that $\mathbf{x}$ has a unique representation of the form $\sum b_i\mathbf{x}_i$ and that $\{\mathbf{x}_1, \mathbf{x}_2, \cdots, \mathbf{x}_n\}^\perp$ by 2.2. This proves 2.3

2.4. DEFINITION OF A BASIS. A set $\{\mathbf{x}_1, \mathbf{x}_2, \cdots, \mathbf{x}_n\}$ of vectors of a vector space V is called a *basis* of V if and only if the vectors $\mathbf{x}_1, \mathbf{x}_2, \cdots, \mathbf{x}_n$ are linearly independent and span V.

Using 2.2, we see that $\{\mathbf{x}_1, \mathbf{x}_2, \cdots, \mathbf{x}_n\}$ is a basis of V if and only if every vector $\mathbf{y}$ of V has a unique representation of the form

$$\mathbf{y} = a_1\mathbf{x}_1 + a_2\mathbf{x}_2 + \cdots + a_n\mathbf{x}_n$$

for some $a_i \in \mathsf{R}$.

Example 1. If $\mathbf{AB}$ and $\mathbf{AC}$ are any two nonzero, nonparallel vectors of V_2, then $\{\mathbf{AB}, \mathbf{AC}\}$ is a basis of V_2. Thus $\mathbf{AB}$ and $\mathbf{AC}$ are independent (why?), and any other vector $\mathbf{AD}$ of V_2 has the unique form

$$\mathbf{AD} = a\mathbf{AB} + b\mathbf{AC}$$

for some $a, b \in \mathsf{R}$, as indicated in Fig. 2.1.

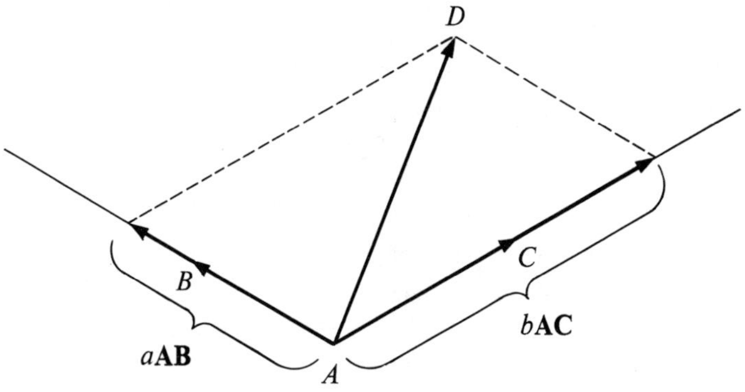

Figure 2.1

Example 2. Are $\mathbf{x}_1 = (2, -1, 0)$, $\mathbf{x}_2 = (1, -1, 1)$, and $\mathbf{x}_3 = (0, 2, 3)$ elements of a basis of R_3?

Solution: We see that $\mathbf{x}_1 - 2\mathbf{x}_2 = (0, 1, -2)$ and hence that $2(\mathbf{x}_1 - 2\mathbf{x}_2) - \mathbf{x}_3 = (0, 0, -7)$ and $3(\mathbf{x}_1 - 2\mathbf{x}_2) + 2\mathbf{x}_3 = (0, 7, 0)$. Also, $\mathbf{x}_1 + \frac{1}{7}(0, 7, 0) = (2, 0, 0)$. Thus the vectors $\mathbf{u}_1 = (1, 0, 0)$, $\mathbf{u}_2 = (0, 1, 0)$, and $\mathbf{u}_3 = (0, 0, 1)$ are in the space spanned by $\mathbf{x}_1$, $\mathbf{x}_2$, and $\mathbf{x}_3$. It follows that $\mathbf{x}_1$, $\mathbf{x}_2$, and $\mathbf{x}_3$ span R_3. To test to see if $\mathbf{x}_1$, $\mathbf{x}_2$, and $\mathbf{x}_3$ are linearly independent, we solve the equation

$$a(2, -1, 0) + b(1, -1, 1) + c(0, 2, 3) = (0, 0, 0)$$

for $a, b, c \in \mathsf{R}$. This equation is equivalent to the system

$$\begin{cases} 2a + b = 0 \\ -a - b + 2c = 0 \\ b + 3c = 0. \end{cases}$$

Thus $b = -2a$ from the first equation, $-a - (-2a) + 2c = 0$, or $a = -2c$, from the second equation, and $-2a + 3c = 0$, or $a = \frac{3}{2}c$, from the third equation. Clearly the only solution is $a = b = c = 0$. Therefore $\{\mathbf{x}_1, \mathbf{x}_2, \mathbf{x}_3\}^{\perp}$ by 2.3, and $\{\mathbf{x}_1, \mathbf{x}_2, \mathbf{x}_3\}$ is a basis of R_3.

As we shall presently show, it is only necessary to do half the work of Example 2 to prove that a set of three vectors is a basis of R_3. That is, we need only show either that the three vectors are linearly independent or that they span R_3. More generally, we shall show that any n linearly independent vectors span R_n and that any n vectors which span R_n are linearly independent.

Example 3. Prove that the three medians of a triangle meet at a point P. Show that P is a point of trisection of each median. Point P is called the *centroid* of the triangle.

Solution: In triangle ABC of Fig. 2.2, D is the midpoint of side BC, E the midpoint of AC, and P the point of intersection of AD and BE. Therefore

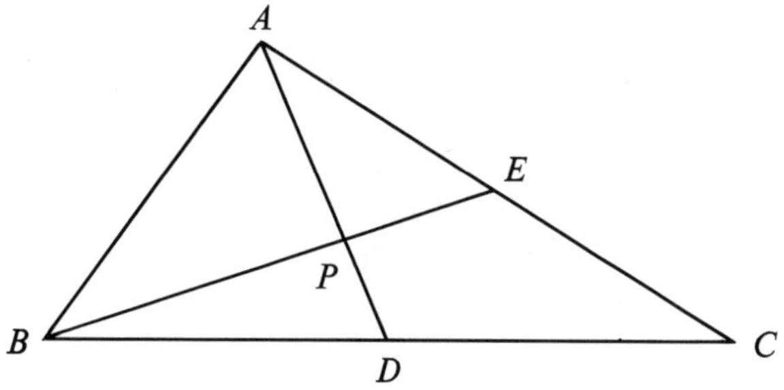

Figure 2.2

$$\mathbf{AD} = \mathbf{AB} + \mathbf{BD} = \mathbf{AB} + \tfrac{1}{2}\mathbf{BC} = \mathbf{AB} + \tfrac{1}{2}(\mathbf{AC} - \mathbf{AB})$$

and

$$\mathbf{AD} = \tfrac{1}{2}(\mathbf{AB} + \mathbf{AC}).$$

Similarly,

$$\mathbf{BE} = \tfrac{1}{2}(\mathbf{BA} + \mathbf{BC}).$$

Since P is on $\mathbf{AD}$ and $\mathbf{BE}$,

$$\mathbf{AP} = r\mathbf{AD}, \quad \mathbf{BP} = s\mathbf{BE} \text{ for some } r, s \in \mathsf{R}.$$

Now

$$\mathbf{BP} = \mathbf{BA} + \mathbf{AP} = \mathbf{BA} + \frac{r}{2}(\mathbf{AB} + \mathbf{AC})$$

$$= \mathbf{BA} + \frac{r}{2}(\mathbf{AB} + \mathbf{AB} + \mathbf{BC})$$

and therefore

(1) $$\mathbf{BP} = (1 - r)\mathbf{BA} + \frac{r}{2}\mathbf{BC}.$$

However, $\mathbf{BP}$ is also given by $\mathbf{BP} = s\mathbf{BE}$ or

(2) $$\mathbf{BP} = \frac{s}{2}\mathbf{BA} + \frac{s}{2}\mathbf{BC}.$$

Since $\{\mathbf{BA}, \mathbf{BC}\}^{\perp}$, we have from (1) and (2) that

$$1 - r = \frac{s}{2}, \quad \frac{r}{2} = \frac{s}{2}.$$

Hence

$$r = s = \tfrac{2}{3}.$$

This proves that P is the point of trisection of both AD and BE away from each vertex. Since AD and BE are any two of the medians of the triangle, it follows that all three medians meet at the point of trisection of each median away from the vertex.

EXERCISES

In each of the following exercises show that the set of vectors is linearly independent, and tell whether it is a basis of the given vector space.

1. $\{(1, 1), (1, -1)\}$ in R_2.
2. $\{(2, -3)\}$ in R_2.
3. $\{(1, 0, 0), (1, 1, 0)\}$ in R_3.
4. $\{(2, 0, 1), (1, 2, 0), (0, 1, 0)\}$ in R_3.
5. $\{(1, 0, 0, 0), (0, 1, 1, 1)\}$ in R_4.
6. $\{(1, 1, 0, 0), (0, 1, 1, 0), (0, 0, 1, 1), (1, 0, 1, 0)\}$ in R_4.
7. $\{(0, 0, 1, 1, 1), (0, 1, 1, 1, 1)\}$ in R_5.
8. $\{\mathbf{u}_1, \mathbf{u}_1 + 2\mathbf{u}_2, \mathbf{u}_1 + 2\mathbf{u}_2 + 3\mathbf{u}_3, \cdots, \mathbf{u}_1 + 2\mathbf{u}_2 + 3\mathbf{u}_3 + \cdots + n\mathbf{u}_n\}$ in R_n, where the $\mathbf{u}_i$'s are as defined on page 19.

3. DIMENSION

Before defining what is meant by the dimension of a vector space, let us prove the following replacement properties.

2.5. REPLACEMENT PROPERTY OF A BASIS. Let $\{\mathbf{x}_1, \mathbf{x}_2, \cdots, \mathbf{x}_n\}$ be a basis of a vector space V and let $\mathbf{y}$ be any nonzero vector of V. If

$$(1) \qquad \mathbf{y} = \sum_{i=1}^{n} a_i\mathbf{x}_i, \qquad a_i \in \mathsf{R},$$

then $a_i \neq 0$ for some i, and if $a_k \neq 0$, then

$$\{\mathbf{x}_1, \cdots, \mathbf{x}_{k-1}, \mathbf{y}, \mathbf{x}_{k+1}, \cdots, \mathbf{x}_n\}$$

is also a basis of V.

Proof: We can solve (1) for $\mathbf{x}_k$, obtaining

$$\mathbf{x}_k = -\frac{1}{a_k}(a_1\mathbf{x}_1 + \cdots + a_{k-1}\mathbf{x}_{k-1} + a_{k+1}\mathbf{x}_{k+1} + \cdots + a_n\mathbf{x}_n - \mathbf{y}).$$

Since $\mathbf{x}_k$ is a linear combination of the other $\mathbf{x}_i$'s and $\mathbf{y}$, every $\mathbf{x}_j$ is a linear combination of the other $\mathbf{x}_i$'s and $\mathbf{y}$. Consequently,

$$V = \mathsf{R}\mathbf{x}_1 + \cdots + \mathsf{R}\mathbf{x}_{k-1} + \mathsf{R}\mathbf{y} + \mathsf{R}\mathbf{x}_{k+1} + \cdots + \mathsf{R}\mathbf{x}_n.$$

Therefore we need only show that $\{\mathbf{x}_1, \cdots, \mathbf{x}_{k-1}, \mathbf{y}, \mathbf{x}_{k+1}, \cdots, \mathbf{x}_n\}^\perp$ to prove 2.5. If

$$\sum_{i=1}^{k-1} b_i\mathbf{x}_i + b\mathbf{y} + \sum_{i=k+1}^{n} b_i\mathbf{x}_i = \mathbf{0} \tag{2}$$

for some $b, b_i \in \mathsf{R}$ and $b = 0$, then all $b_i = 0$ since $\{\mathbf{x}_1, \cdots, \mathbf{x}_{k-1}, \mathbf{x}_{k+1}, \cdots, \mathbf{x}_n\}^\perp$. If $b \neq 0$, then we can solve (2) for $\mathbf{y}$, obtaining

$$\mathbf{y} = -\frac{1}{b}\left(\sum_{i=1}^{k-1} b_i\mathbf{x}_i + \sum_{i=k+1}^{n} b_i\mathbf{x}_i\right). \tag{3}$$

Now (1) and (3) should be the same, since the representation of $\mathbf{y}$ as a linear combination of $\mathbf{x}_1, \mathbf{x}_2, \cdots, \mathbf{x}_n$ is unique by 2.2. Clearly (1) and (3) are not the same, for $a_k \neq 0$ in (1), whereas the coefficient of $\mathbf{x}_k$ is 0 in (3). This contradiction shows that $b = 0$ and hence all $b_i = 0$ in (2). Thus

$$\{\mathbf{x}_1, \cdots, \mathbf{x}_{k-1}, \mathbf{y}, \mathbf{x}_{k+1}, \cdots, \mathbf{x}_n\}^\perp$$

and 2.5 is proved.

We can extend the replacement property to several vectors as follows.

2.6. EXTENDED REPLACEMENT PROPERTY OF A BASIS. Let $\{\mathbf{x}_1, \mathbf{x}_2, \cdots, \mathbf{x}_n\}$ be a basis of a vector space V and let $\mathbf{y}_1, \mathbf{y}_2, \cdots, \mathbf{y}_k$ be any k linearly independent vectors of V. Then necessarily $k \leq n$ and V has a basis made up of the k y_i's and $n - k$ of the x_i's.

Proof: If $k = 1$, then 2.6 is simply 2.5. Assume that $1 \leq m < k$ and that there is a basis of V of the form $\{\mathbf{y}_1, \cdots, \mathbf{y}_m, \mathbf{z}_1, \cdots, \mathbf{z}_{n-m}\}$, where $\{\mathbf{z}_1, \cdots, \mathbf{z}_{n-m}\} \subset \{\mathbf{x}_1, \cdots, \mathbf{x}_n\}$. Now $\mathbf{y}_{m+1}$ is a linear combination of this basis,

$$\mathbf{y}_{m+1} = \sum_{i=1}^{m} a_i\mathbf{y}_i + \sum_{i=1}^{n-m} b_i\mathbf{z}_i,$$

with some $a_i \neq 0$ or $b_i \neq 0$. We cannot have all $b_i = 0$, for then some $a_i \neq 0$ and $\mathsf{R}\mathbf{y}_{m+1} \cap (\mathsf{R}\mathbf{y}_1 + \cdots + \mathsf{R}\mathbf{y}_m) \neq \{\mathbf{0}\}$ contrary to $\{\mathbf{y}_1, \cdots, \mathbf{y}_{m+1}\}^{\perp}$. Therefore by 2.5 we can replace some $\mathbf{z}_i$ by $\mathbf{y}_{m+1}$ to obtain a new basis of V of the form $\{\mathbf{y}_1, \cdots, \mathbf{y}_{m+1}, \mathbf{w}_1, \cdots, \mathbf{w}_{n-m-1}\}$, where $\{\mathbf{w}_1, \cdots, \mathbf{w}_{n-m-1}\} \subset \{\mathbf{x}_1, \cdots, \mathbf{x}_n\}$. Continuing this process of inserting one more $\mathbf{y}_i$ in a basis of V, we eventually find a basis with n elements, k of which are $\mathbf{y}_1, \mathbf{y}_2, \cdots, \mathbf{y}_k$. Consequently, $k \leq n$ and 2.6 is proved.

There are many bases of a vector space V. However, if $\{\mathbf{u}_1, \mathbf{u}_2, \cdots, \mathbf{u}_r\}$ and $\{\mathbf{v}_1, \mathbf{v}_2, \cdots, \mathbf{v}_s\}$ are two bases of V, then by letting the $\mathbf{u}_i$'s be x's and the $\mathbf{v}_i$'s be $\mathbf{y}$'s in 2.6, we have that $s \leq r$. Interchanging the roles of the $\mathbf{u}_i$'s and $\mathbf{v}_i$'s, we have $r \leq s$. Therefore $r = s$. That is, the number of vectors in a basis of V is an *invariant* of V; in other words, if one basis of V has r elements, then all bases of V have r elements.

2.7. DEFINITION OF DIMENSION. If a vector space V has n elements in a basis, then n is called the *dimension* of V and we write

$$\dim V = n.$$

There are vector spaces having an infinite number of elements in a basis, but we shall not consider such spaces in this book.

In view of the extended replacement property, every set of n linearly independent vectors of an n-dimensional vector space V is a basis. Also, every set having more than n vectors is dependent. By 2.7, any set of linearly independent vectors of V can be extended to a basis of V. The subspace $\{\mathbf{0}\}$ of every vector space is said to have dimension 0.

The vector space V_2 has a basis consisting of two vectors by Example 1, page 27. Therefore $\dim V_2 = 2$. If $\mathbf{x}_1$, $\mathbf{x}_2$, and $\mathbf{x}_3$ are any three noncoplanar vectors of V_3, then they are linearly independent (why?) and span V_3. Thus any $\mathbf{x} \in V_3$ is a linear combination

$$\mathbf{x} = a\mathbf{x}_1 + b\mathbf{x}_2 + c\mathbf{x}_3$$

of $\mathbf{x}_1$, $\mathbf{x}_2$, and $\mathbf{x}_3$, as shown in Fig. 2.3. It follows that dim $V_3 = 3$, as expected.

The vectors $\mathbf{u}_1, \mathbf{u}_2, \cdots, \mathbf{u}_n$ of R_n defined on page 19 are linearly independent and span R_n. Hence $\{\mathbf{u}_1, \mathbf{u}_2, \cdots, \mathbf{u}_n\}$ is a basis of R_n, and we conclude that

$$\dim \mathsf{R}_n = n$$

for every positive integer n.

Example 1. Extend the set $\{(1, -1, 1), (4, 3, -3)\}$ to a basis of R_3.

Solution: The vectors $(1, -1, 1)$ and $(4, 3, -3)$ are linearly independent, since $\mathsf{R}(1, -1, 1) \cap \mathsf{R}(4, 3, -3) = \{\mathbf{0}\}$. Therefore these two vectors together with one more vector form a basis of R_3. We may select this third vector more or less at random, checking only to be sure it is not in $\mathsf{R}(1, -1, 1) + \mathsf{R}(4, 3, -3)$. In particular, we can use at least one of the $\mathbf{u}_i$'s in view of 2.6 and the fact that $\{\mathbf{u}_1, \mathbf{u}_2, \mathbf{u}_3\}$ is a basis of R_3. We cannot use $\mathbf{u}_1 = (1, 0, 0)$, since $\mathbf{u}_1 \in \mathsf{R}(1, -1, 1) + \mathsf{R}(4, 3, -3)$,

$$\mathbf{u}_1 = \tfrac{3}{7}(1, -1, 1) + \tfrac{1}{7}(4, 3, -3).$$

Now $\{(1, -1, 1), (4, 3, -3), (0, 1, 0)\}^{\perp}$, because

$$a(1, -1, 1) + b(4, 3, -3) + c(0, 1, 0) = (0, 0, 0)$$

if and only if

$$\begin{cases} a + 4b \qquad = 0 \\ -a + 3b + c = 0 \\ a - 3b \qquad = 0, \end{cases}$$

or $a = b = c = 0$. Therefore $\{(1, -1, 1), (4, 3, -3), (0, 1, 0)\}$ is a basis of R_3. It may easily be shown that $\{(1, -1, 1), (4, 3, -3), (0, 0, 1)\}$ is also a basis of R_3.

Example 2. If $\mathbf{x}_1 = (1, 0, 0, 0)$, $\mathbf{x}_2 = (1, 1, 0, 0)$, $\mathbf{x}_3 = (1, 1, 1, 0)$, $\mathbf{x}_4 = (1, 1, 1, 1)$, then is $\{\mathbf{x}_1, \mathbf{x}_2, \mathbf{x}_3, \mathbf{x}_4\}$ a basis of R_4?

Solution: The only solution of the equation

$$a\mathbf{x}_1 + b\mathbf{x}_2 + c\mathbf{x}_3 + d\mathbf{x}_4 = (0, 0, 0, 0)$$

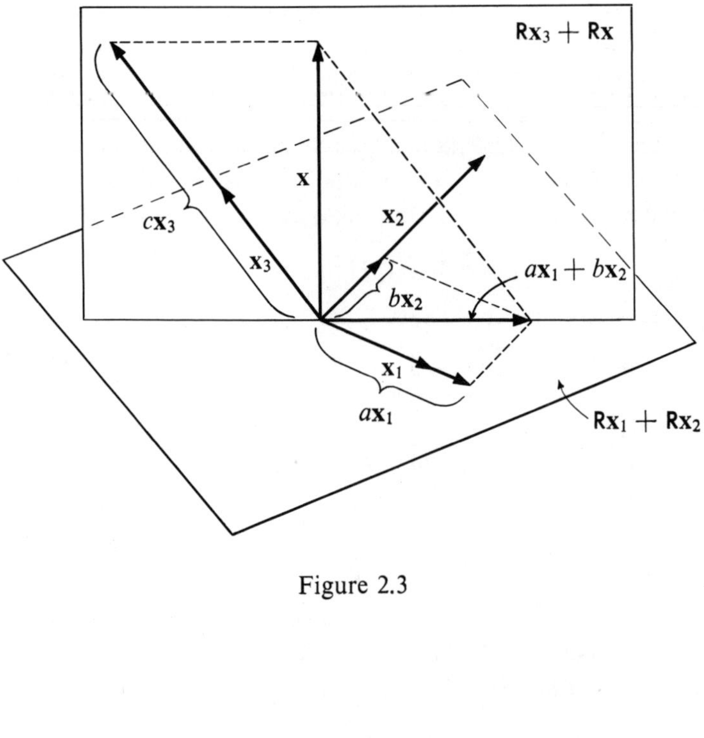

Figure 2.3

is easily shown to be $a = b = c = d = 0$. Hence $\{\mathbf{x}_1, \mathbf{x}_2, \mathbf{x}_3, \mathbf{x}_4\}^\perp$ by 2.3. Since dim $\mathsf{R}_4 = 4$, every set of four linearly independent vectors is a basis. Hence $\{\mathbf{x}_1, \mathbf{x}_2, \mathbf{x}_3, \mathbf{x}_4\}$ is a basis of R_4.

Example 3. Prove that the vectors joining each vertex of a tetrahedron to the centroid of the opposite face meet at a point P. Does P divide each of these vectors in the same ratio? If so, what is the ratio? Point P is called the *centroid* of the tetrahedron. (See Example 3, page 28, for a similar problem.)

Solution: Let $ABCD$ be a tetrahedron (Fig. 2.4), E the centroid of face BCD, F the centroid of face ABD, and P the point of intersection of AE and CF. Then

$$\mathbf{CE} = \tfrac{2}{3}\mathbf{CH} = \tfrac{1}{3}(\mathbf{CB} + \mathbf{CD})$$

by Example 3, page 28, and similarly

$$\mathbf{AF} = \tfrac{1}{3}(\mathbf{AB} + \mathbf{AD}).$$

Now

$$\begin{aligned}\mathbf{AE} &= \mathbf{AC} + \mathbf{CE} = \mathbf{AC} + \tfrac{1}{3}(\mathbf{CB} + \mathbf{CD})\\ &= \mathbf{AC} + \tfrac{1}{3}(\mathbf{CA} + \mathbf{AB} + \mathbf{CA} + \mathbf{AD})\\ &= \tfrac{1}{3}(\mathbf{AB} + \mathbf{AC} + \mathbf{AD})\end{aligned}$$

and similarly

$$\mathbf{CF} = \tfrac{1}{3}(\mathbf{CA} + \mathbf{CB} + \mathbf{CD}).$$

Since point P is on AE and CF,

$$\mathbf{AP} = r\mathbf{AE}, \quad \mathbf{CP} = s\mathbf{CF} \text{ for some } r, s \in \mathsf{R}.$$

Hence

$$\mathbf{AP} = \frac{r}{3}\mathbf{AB} + \frac{r}{3}\mathbf{AC} + \frac{r}{3}\mathbf{AD}. \tag{1}$$

Also,

$$\begin{aligned}\mathbf{AP} &= \mathbf{AC} + \mathbf{CP}\\ &= \mathbf{AC} + \frac{s}{3}(\mathbf{CA} + \mathbf{CB} + \mathbf{CD})\\ &= \mathbf{AC} + \frac{s}{3}(\mathbf{CA} + \mathbf{CA} + \mathbf{AB} + \mathbf{CA} + \mathbf{AD})\end{aligned}$$

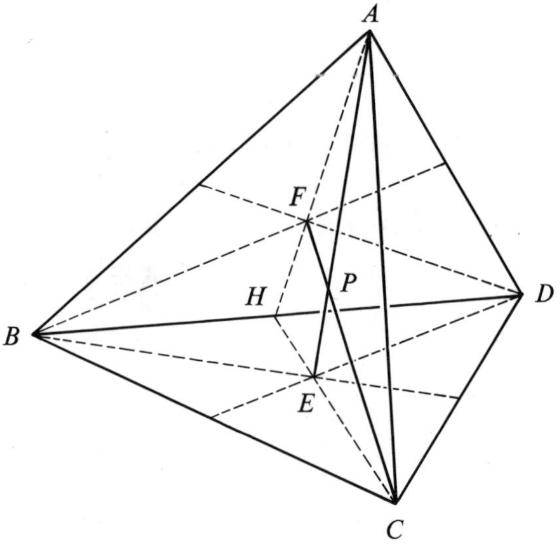

Figure 2.4

and

$$\mathbf{AP} = \frac{s}{3}\mathbf{AB} + (1 - s)\mathbf{AC} + \frac{s}{3}\mathbf{AD}. \tag{2}$$

The vectors **AB**, **AC**, and **AD** are noncoplanar and therefore form a basis of V_3. Consequently, the two representations of **AP** in (1) and (2) above must coincide; i.e.,

$$\frac{r}{3} = \frac{s}{3}, \quad \frac{r}{3} = 1 - s, \quad \frac{r}{3} = \frac{s}{3}.$$

Hence

$$r = s = \tfrac{3}{4}.$$

This shows that the point P divides each of the segments AE and CF in the same ratio of 3/4:

$$\mathbf{AP} = \tfrac{3}{4}\mathbf{AE}, \quad \mathbf{CP} = \tfrac{3}{4}\mathbf{CF}.$$

Since AE and CF were any two medians of the tetrahedron, it follows that all four medians meet at the same point P three-fourths of the distance from the vertex to the face.

EXERCISES

In each of Exercises 1–8 show that the set of vectors is linearly independent and then extend each set, if necessary, to a basis of the given vector space.

1. $\{(1, 1), (4, -4)\}$ in R_2.
2. $\{(1, 2, 3), (2, 3, 1)\}$ in R_3.
3. $\{(-1, 5, -5), (0, 5, -5), (0, 0, -5)\}$ in R_3.
4. $\{(1, -1, 1, -1), (-1, 1, 1, -1)\}$ in R_4.
5. $\{(1, 0, 0, 0), (1, 0, 1, 0), (1, 0, 0, 1), (1, 1, 1, 1)\}$ in R_4.
6. $\{(1, 1, 0, 0), (1, -1, 0, 0), (1, 0, 1, 0)\}$ in R_4.
7. $\{(1, 0, 0, 0, 1), (0, 1, 0, 1, 0), (0, 0, 1, 0, 0)\}$ in R_5.
8. $\{(1, 0, 1, 0, 1), (0, 1, 0, 1, 0), (1, 0, 0, 1, 0)\}$ in R_5.
9. Describe a one-dimensional vector space.

10. Let V be an n-dimensional space and let S be a subspace, $S \neq \{\mathbf{0}\}$. Prove that $\dim S = k \leq n$, with $\dim S = n$ if and only if $S = V$.
11. Let V be an n-dimensional vector space. Prove that for every subspace S of V there exists a subspace S' such that $S \cap S' = \{\mathbf{0}\}$ and $S + S' = V$. (We call S' a *complement* of S.) Show that S' is not unique if S is a proper subspace.
12. We call $\{\mathbf{x}_1, \mathbf{x}_2, \cdots, \mathbf{x}_k\}$ a set of *generators* of a vector space V if the vectors $\mathbf{x}_1, \mathbf{x}_2, \cdots, \mathbf{x}_k$ span V. Prove that some subset of a set of generators of V is actually a basis of V.

In each of Exercises 13–15 show that the set of vectors is a set of generators of the given vector space. Find a subset of the set which is a basis.

13. $\{(1, -1), (-3, 3), (2, 1)\}$ in R_2.
14. $\{(1, 1, 0), (-1, 0, 1), (0, 1, 1), (1, 1, 1)\}$ in R_3.
15. $\{(1, -1, 1, -1), (-1, 1, -1, 1), (2, -1, 2, -1), (-3, 1, -3, 1), (1, 1, -2, -2), (2, 2, -1, -1), (1, -2, -2, 1)\}$ in R_4.
16. If S and T are subspaces of an n-dimensional vector space V, then prove that

$$\dim(S + T) = \dim S + \dim T - \dim(S \cap T).$$

[*Hint:* If $S \cap T \neq \{\mathbf{0}\}$, extend a basis $\{\mathbf{x}_1, \cdots, \mathbf{x}_k\}$ of $S \cap T$ to a basis $\{\mathbf{x}_1, \cdots, \mathbf{x}_k, \mathbf{y}_1, \cdots, \mathbf{y}_m\}$ of S and a basis $\{\mathbf{x}_1, \cdots, \mathbf{x}_k, \mathbf{z}_1, \cdots, \mathbf{z}_t\}$ of T. Show that $\{\mathbf{x}_1, \cdots, \mathbf{x}_k, \mathbf{y}_1, \cdots, \mathbf{y}_m, \mathbf{z}_1, \cdots, \mathbf{z}_t\}$ is a basis of $S + T$. Modify the argument slightly if $S \cap T = \{\mathbf{0}\}$.]

4. HOMOMORPHISMS

If A and B are any two sets, then the notation

$$A \xrightarrow{f} B$$

will be used to show that f is a *mapping* of set A into set B. Thus corresponding to each $a \in A$ is a unique element of B, denoted by $f(a)$. In the language of functions, f is a function whose domain is A and whose range is B.

2.8 DEFINITION OF A HOMOMORPHISM. If V and W are vector spaces and $V \xrightarrow{f} W$ is a mapping, then f is called a homomorphism if and only if

(1) $$f(\mathbf{x} + \mathbf{y}) = f(\mathbf{x}) + f(\mathbf{y}) \text{ for all } \mathbf{x}, \mathbf{y} \in V.$$

(2) $$f(a\mathbf{x}) = af(\mathbf{x}) \text{ for all } \mathbf{x} \in V,\ a \in \mathsf{R}.$$

According to this definition, sums in V are mapped into sums in W, and scalar multiplication is preserved by a homomorphism.

If $V \xrightarrow{f} W$ is a homorphism, then

$$\mathbf{0} + f(\mathbf{x}) = f(\mathbf{x}) = f(\mathbf{x} + \mathbf{0}) = f(\mathbf{x}) + f(\mathbf{0})$$

and $\mathbf{0} = f(\mathbf{0})$ by the cancellation law. That is, the zero vector of V is mapped into the zero vector of W by f. If we let $a = -1$ in 2.8(2), then we get

$$f(-\mathbf{x}) = -f(\mathbf{x}) \text{ for all } \mathbf{x} \in V.$$

We can easily extend 2.8(1) to more than two summands. For example,

$$\begin{aligned} f(\mathbf{x} + \mathbf{y} + \mathbf{z}) &= f[(\mathbf{x} + \mathbf{y}) + \mathbf{z}] \\ &= f(\mathbf{x} + \mathbf{y}) + f(\mathbf{z}) \\ &= f(\mathbf{x}) + f(\mathbf{y}) + f(\mathbf{z}). \end{aligned}$$

More generally, if $\mathbf{x}_1, \mathbf{x}_2, \cdots, \mathbf{x}_n$ are vectors of V and $a_1, a_2, \cdots, a_n$ are scalars, then

2.9 $$f\left(\sum_{i=1}^{n} a_i\mathbf{x}_i\right) = \sum_{i=1}^{n} a_i f(\mathbf{x}_i).$$

Thus

$$\begin{aligned} f\left(\sum_{i=1}^{n} a_i\mathbf{x}_i\right) &= \sum_{i=1}^{n} f(a_i\mathbf{x}_i) && \text{by 2.8(1)} \\ &= \sum_{i=1}^{n} a_i f(\mathbf{x}_i) && \text{by 2.8(2).} \end{aligned}$$

If $V \xrightarrow{f} W$ is a homomorphism, then we call V the *domain* of f,

$$V = \operatorname{dom} f,$$

and we call the subset of W into which V is mapped the *image* of f,

$$\operatorname{im} f = \{f(\mathbf{x}) \mid \mathbf{x} \in V\}.$$

It is clear by 2.9 that $\operatorname{im} f$ is a subspace of W.

A mapping $V \xrightarrow{f} W$ is said to be a 1–1 *mapping* if distinct elements of V are mapped into distinct elements of W; i.e., whenever $\mathbf{x} \neq \mathbf{y}$ in V, then $f(\mathbf{x}) \neq f(\mathbf{y})$ in W.

2.10. DEFINITION OF AN ISOMORPHISM. A homomorphism $V \xrightarrow{f} W$ is called an *isomorphism* if and only if f is a 1–1 mapping and $\operatorname{im} f = W$.

Two vector spaces V and W are called *isomorphic* if there exists an isomorphism $V \xrightarrow{f} W$ (or $W \xrightarrow{g} V$).

2.11. THEOREM. Two finite-dimensional vector spaces V and W are isomorphic if and only if $\dim V = \dim W$.

Proof: Let $V \xrightarrow{f} W$ be an isomorphism and let $\{\mathbf{x}_1, \mathbf{x}_2, \cdots, \mathbf{x}_n\}$ be a basis of V. Since $\operatorname{im} f = W$, each vector in W has the form $f(\mathbf{y})$ for some $\mathbf{y} \in V$. If

$$\mathbf{y} = \sum_{i=1}^{n} a_i \mathbf{x}_i,$$

then

$$f(\mathbf{y}) = \sum_{i=1}^{n} a_i f(\mathbf{x}_i)$$

by 2.9. Therefore $\{f(\mathbf{x}_1), f(\mathbf{x}_2), \cdots, f(\mathbf{x}_n)\}$ is a set of generators of W. Is it an independent set? To answer this question, suppose

$$\sum_{i=1}^{n} b_i f(\mathbf{x}_i) = \mathbf{0}.$$

Then

$$f\left(\sum_{i=1}^{n} b_i \mathbf{x}_i\right) = f(\mathbf{0}) \quad \text{and} \quad \sum_{i=1}^{n} b_i \mathbf{x}_i = \mathbf{0}$$

since f is a 1–1 mapping. The vectors $\mathbf{x}_1, \mathbf{x}_2, \cdots, \mathbf{x}_n$ are linearly independent and therefore $b_1 = 0, b_2 = 0, \cdots, b_n = 0$ by 2.3. In turn, this proves that the vectors $f(\mathbf{x}_1)$, $f(\mathbf{x}_2)$, $\cdots$, $f(\mathbf{x}_n)$ are linearly independent. Consequently, $\{f(\mathbf{x}_1), f(\mathbf{x}_2), \cdots, f(\mathbf{x}_n)\}$ is a basis of W and dim $V =$ dim W.

Conversely, assume that dim $V =$ dim $W = n$, and let $\{\mathbf{u}_1, \mathbf{u}_2, \cdots, \mathbf{u}_n\}$ and $\{\mathbf{v}_1, \mathbf{v}_2, \cdots, \mathbf{v}_n\}$ be bases of V and W, respectively. Define the mapping f by

$$f\left(\sum_{i=1}^{n} a_i\mathbf{u}_i\right) = \sum_{i=1}^{n} a_i\mathbf{v}_i \text{ for all } a_i \in \mathsf{R}.$$

Thus, by definition, dom $f = V$ and im $f = W$. If $\mathbf{x}, \mathbf{y} \in V$, then

$$\mathbf{x} = \sum_{i=1}^{n} b_i\mathbf{u}_i, \quad \mathbf{y} = \sum_{i=1}^{n} c_i\mathbf{u}_i$$

for some $b_i, c_i \in \mathsf{R}$. Therefore

$$\mathbf{x} + \mathbf{y} = \sum_{i=1}^{n} (b_i + c_i)\mathbf{u}_i$$

and

$$\begin{aligned} f(\mathbf{x} + \mathbf{y}) &= \sum_{i=1}^{n} (b_i + c_i)\mathbf{v}_i \\ &= \sum_{i=1}^{n} b_i\mathbf{v}_i + \sum_{i=1}^{n} c_i\mathbf{v}_i \\ &= f(\mathbf{x}) + f(\mathbf{y}). \end{aligned}$$

Similarly, for every $a \in \mathsf{R}$,

$$a\mathbf{x} = \sum_{i=1}^{n} ab_i\mathbf{u}_i$$

and

$$\begin{aligned} f(a\mathbf{x}) &= \sum_{i=1}^{n} ab_i\mathbf{v}_i \\ &= a\sum_{i=1}^{n} b_i\mathbf{v}_i \\ &= a\, f(\mathbf{x}). \end{aligned}$$

This proves that f is a homomorphism. Whenever $\mathbf{x} \neq \mathbf{y}$, then $b_i \neq c_i$ for some i in the above representations of $\mathbf{x}$ and $\mathbf{y}$, and hence $f(\mathbf{x}) \neq f(\mathbf{y})$. Therefore f is an isomorphism and 2.11 is proved.

Isomorphic vector spaces are algebraically identical. That is, those properties involving only addition and scalar multiplication are exactly the same in two isomorphic vector spaces. Therefore two vector spaces having the same dimension are algebraically identical, according to 2.11. In other words, if dim $V = \dim W$, then the only way we can distinguish between V and W is by the nature of their elements, not by any mathematical means.

The vector spaces V_2 and R_2 are two-dimensional and therefore isomorphic. Similarly, the vector spaces V_3 and R_3 are isomorphic, both being three-dimensional.

The isomorphism between V_2 and R_2 may be realized as follows. First, select a rectangular coordinate system in E_2. Then the endpoints of each vector have coordinates which uniquely determine the vector. A vector, such as **OC** in Fig. 2.5, which has its initial point at the origin is called a *position vector*. Any other vector **AB** may be compared to a position vector by selecting new x'- and y'-axes having the same direction as the x- and y-axes, respectively, and having A as the new origin (Fig. 2.5). If A, B, and C have respective coordinates (a_1, a_2), (b_1, b_2), and (c_1, c_2), then clearly $\mathbf{AB} = \mathbf{OC}$ if and only if $c_1 = b_1 - a_1$ and $c_2 = b_2 - a_2$. In terms of elements of V_2 and R_2,

$$\mathbf{AB} = \mathbf{OC} \text{ if and only if } (c_1, c_2) = (b_1 - a_1, b_2 - a_2).$$

Given a vector **AB** whose initial point and terminal point have coordinates (a_1, a_2) and (b_1, b_2), respectively, we shall call the ordered pair of numbers $(b_1 - a_1, b_2 - a_2)$ the *components* of **AB**. The components of a position vector **OC** are simply the coordinates of its endpoint C. It is clear from our discussion above that two vectors of V_2 are equal if and only if they have the same components.

We now have a natural way to map V_2 into R_2,

$$V_2 \xrightarrow{f} \mathsf{R}_2, \text{ where } f(\mathbf{x}) = (c_1, c_2), \text{ the components of } \mathbf{x}.$$

If $f(\mathbf{x}) = (a_1, a_2)$ and $f(\mathbf{y}) = (b_1, b_2)$, then

$$f(\mathbf{x} + \mathbf{y}) = (a_1 + b_1, a_2 + b_2)$$

because opposite sides of the quadrilateral $OACB$ in Fig. 2.6 have the same components and hence are equal. Since $(a_1 + b_1, a_2 + b_2) = (a_1, a_2) + (b_1, b_2)$ in the vector space R_2, we have proved that

$$(1) \qquad f(\mathbf{x} + \mathbf{y}) = (a_1, a_2) + (b_1, b_2) = f(\mathbf{x}) + f(\mathbf{y}).$$

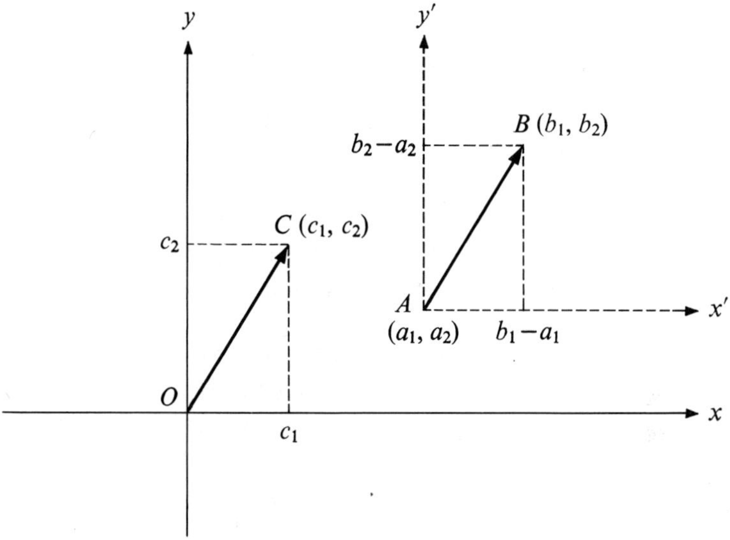

Figure 2.5

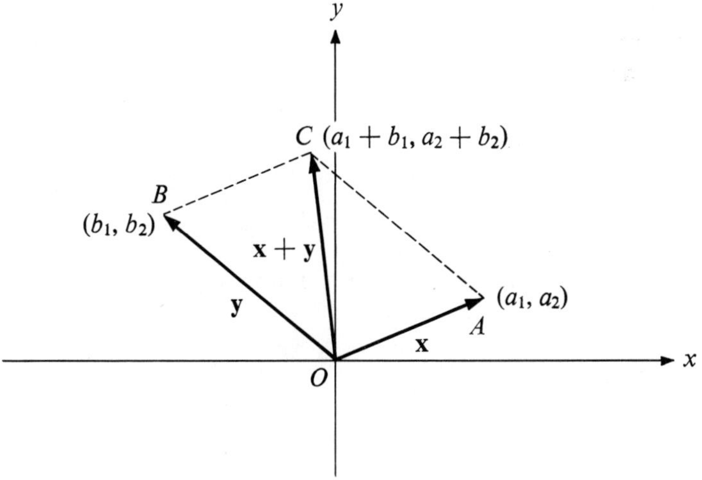

Figure 2.6

If vector $\mathbf{x}$ has components (a_1, a_2), then vector $r\mathbf{x}$ has components (ra_1, ra_2) for each $r \in \mathsf{R}$. Thus in Fig. 2.7

$$d(O, A) = \sqrt{a_1^2 + a_2^2}, \quad d(O, B) = \sqrt{r^2a_1^2 + r^2a_2^2} = |r|d(O, A),$$

and the directions of $\mathbf{OA}$ and $\mathbf{OB}$ are the same if $r > 0$ and opposite if $r < 0$. Since $(ra_1, ra_2) = r(a_1, a_2)$ in R_2,

$$(2) \qquad f(r\mathbf{x}) = r(a_1, a_2) = rf(\mathbf{x}).$$

Now (1) and (2) are precisely the two properties of a homomorphism (2.8). Since f is a 1–1 mapping and im $f = \mathsf{R}_2$, f is actually an isomosphism.

The above arguments for realizing the isomorphism between V_2 and R_2 can be carried over intact to V_3 and R_3. Thus we select a rectangular coordinate system in E_3 so that each vector $\mathbf{AB}$ has coordinates (a_1, a_2, a_3) and (b_1, b_2, b_3) for its initial point A and terminal point B, respectively. If we call $(b_1 - a_1, b_2 - a_2, b_3 - a_3)$ the *components* of $\mathbf{AB}$, then two vectors of V_3 are equal if and only if they have the same components. The mapping f defined by

$$V_3 \xrightarrow{f} \mathsf{R}_3, \quad f(\mathbf{x}) = (c_1, c_2, c_3), \text{ the components of } \mathbf{x},$$

is shown to be an isomorphism in exactly the same way as it was shown above for V_2 and R_2.

The mapping $V_2 \xrightarrow{f} \mathsf{R}_2$ carries the vectors $\mathbf{i}$ and $\mathbf{j}$ of Fig. 2.8 into $\mathbf{u}_1 = (1, 0)$ and $\mathbf{u}_2 = (0, 1)$, respectively, of R_2,

$$f(\mathbf{i}) = \mathbf{u}_1, \quad f(\mathbf{j}) = \mathbf{u}_2.$$

For each $\mathbf{x} \in V_2$ with components (a_1, a_2), we have

$$\mathbf{x} = a_1\mathbf{i} + a_2\mathbf{j}, \quad f(\mathbf{x}) = a_1\mathbf{u}_1 + a_2\mathbf{u}_2,$$

as shown in Fig. 2.8. That is, the isomorphism f carries the basis $\{\mathbf{i}, \mathbf{j}\}$ of V_2 into the basis $\{\mathbf{u}_1, \mathbf{u}_2\}$ of R_2.

Similarly, the mapping $V_3 \xrightarrow{f} \mathsf{R}_3$ carries the vectors $\mathbf{i}$, $\mathbf{j}$, and $\mathbf{k}$ of Fig. 2.9 into the vectors

$$\mathbf{u}_1 = (1, 0, 0), \quad \mathbf{u}_2 = (0, 1, 0), \quad \mathbf{u}_3 = (0, 0, 1)$$

of R_3:

$$f(\mathbf{i}) = \mathbf{u}_1, \quad f(\mathbf{j}) = \mathbf{u}_2, \quad f(\mathbf{k}) = \mathbf{u}_3.$$

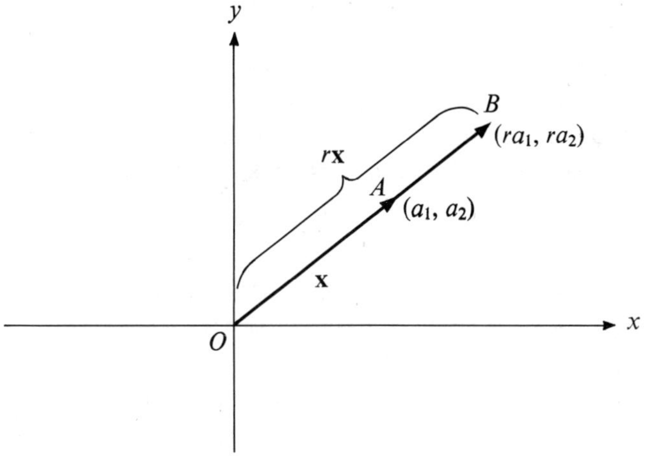

Figure 2.7

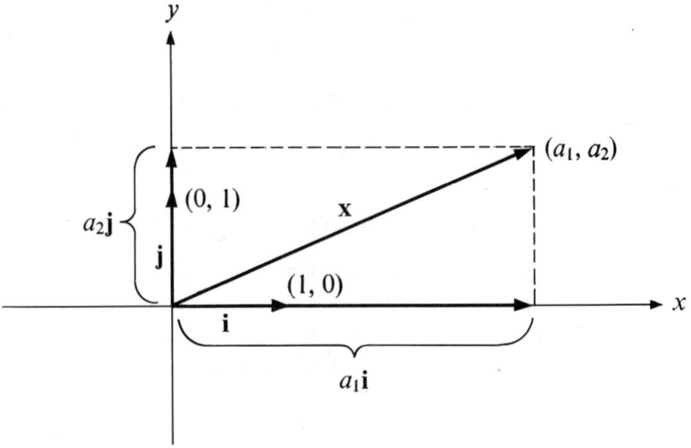

Figure 2.8

If $\mathbf{x} \in V_3$ has components (a_1, a_2, a_3), then

$$\mathbf{x} = a_1\mathbf{i} + a_2\mathbf{j} + a_3\mathbf{k}, \quad f(\mathbf{x}) = a_1\mathbf{u}_1 + a_2\mathbf{u}_2 + a_3\mathbf{u}_3,$$

as shown in Fig. 2.9.

Example 1. If A and B have respective coordinates $(-1, 3)$ and $(4, -5)$, then express the vector $\mathbf{AB} \in V_2$ in terms of the basis $\{\mathbf{i}, \mathbf{j}\}$.

Solution: Vector $\mathbf{AB}$ has components $(4 - (-1), -5 - 3)$, or $(5, -8)$. Since $(5, -8) = 5\mathbf{u}_1 - 8\mathbf{u}_2$ in R_2, we must have

$$\mathbf{AB} = 5\mathbf{i} - 8\mathbf{j}.$$

Example 2. If A and B have respective coordinates $(3, 0, -4)$ and $(7, -7, 5)$, then express the vector $\mathbf{AB} \in V_3$ in terms of the basis $\{\mathbf{i}, \mathbf{j}, \mathbf{k}\}$.

Solution: Vector $\mathbf{AB}$ has components $(7 - 3, -7 - 0, 5 - (-4))$, or $(4, -7, 9)$. Since $(4, -7, 9) = 4\mathbf{u}_1 - 7\mathbf{u}_2 + 9\mathbf{u}_3$ in R_3, we have

$$\mathbf{AB} = 4\mathbf{i} - 7\mathbf{j} + 9\mathbf{k}.$$

Example 3. Prove that an isosceles triangle has two medians of the same length.

Solution: Let us place the triangle in a coordinate plane as shown in Fig. 2.10. Assume that $|\mathbf{OA}| = |\mathbf{AB}|$ and that C is the midpoint of OA and D the midpoint of AB. Then

$$\mathbf{OA} = a\mathbf{i} + b\mathbf{j}, \quad \mathbf{AB} = (c - a)\mathbf{i} - b\mathbf{j},$$

$$\mathbf{CA} = \tfrac{1}{2}(a\mathbf{i} + b\mathbf{j}), \quad \mathbf{AD} = \tfrac{1}{2}[(c - a)\mathbf{i} - b\mathbf{j}].$$

Hence

$$\mathbf{OD} = \mathbf{OA} + \mathbf{AD} = \tfrac{1}{2}[(c + a)\mathbf{i} + b\mathbf{j}],$$

$$\mathbf{CB} = \mathbf{CA} + \mathbf{AB} = \tfrac{1}{2}[(2c - a)\mathbf{i} - b\mathbf{j}].$$

By assumption, $|\mathbf{OA}|^2 = a^2 + b^2 = |\mathbf{AB}|^2 = (c - a)^2 + b^2$, and therefore $c^2 - 2ac = 0$. Clearly $|\mathbf{OD}| = |\mathbf{CB}|$ if and only if

$$(c + a)^2 = (2c - a)^2, \quad \text{or} \quad 3c^2 - 6ac = 0.$$

Hence $|\mathbf{OD}| = |\mathbf{CB}|$ if $|\mathbf{OA}| = |\mathbf{AB}|$.

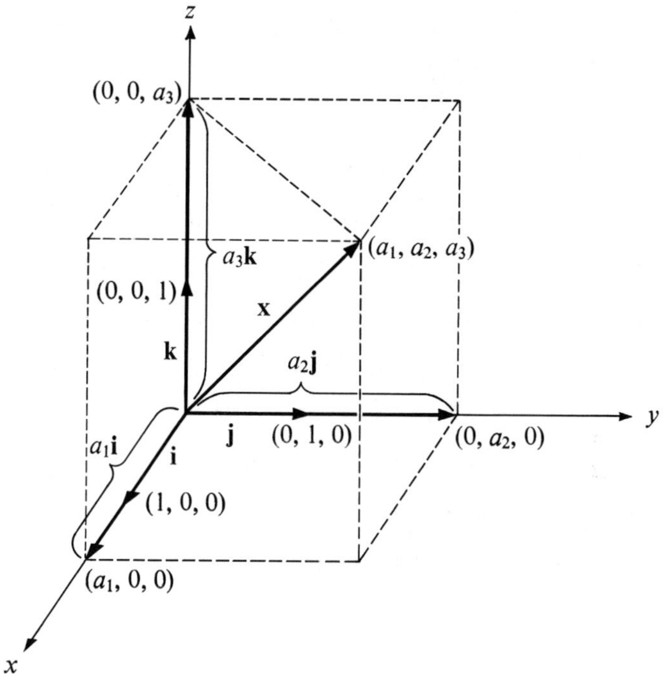

Figure 2.9

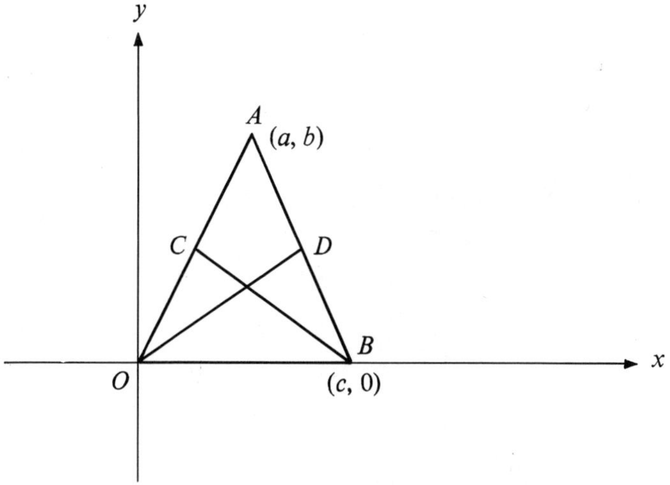

Figure 2.10

Example 4. Prove that the three segments joining the midpoints of opposite sides of a tetrahedron have a point in common which bisects each segment.

Solution: Let us select a coordinate system relative to the tetrahedron as shown in Fig. 2.11. Then we have

$$\mathbf{OA} = a_1\mathbf{i} + a_2\mathbf{j} + a_3\mathbf{k}, \quad \mathbf{AB} = -a_1\mathbf{i} + (b - a_2)\mathbf{j} - a_3\mathbf{k},$$

$$\mathbf{OC} = c_1\mathbf{i} + c_2\mathbf{j}, \quad \mathbf{CB} = -c_1\mathbf{i} + (b - c_2)\mathbf{j}.$$

Hence if D is the midpoint of OA and E the midpoint of BC, then

$$\mathbf{OD} = \tfrac{1}{2}(a_1\mathbf{i} + a_2\mathbf{j} + a_3\mathbf{k}), \quad \mathbf{CE} = \tfrac{1}{2}[-c_1\mathbf{i} + (b - c_2)\mathbf{j}],$$

$$\mathbf{DE} = \mathbf{OE} - \mathbf{OD} = \mathbf{OC} + \mathbf{CE} - \mathbf{OD}$$

$$= \tfrac{1}{2}[(c_1 - a_1)\mathbf{i} + (b + c_2 - a_2)\mathbf{j} - a_3\mathbf{k}].$$

If F is the midpoint of DE, then

$$\mathbf{OF} = \mathbf{OD} + \mathbf{DF} = \mathbf{OD} + \tfrac{1}{2}\mathbf{DE}$$

$$= \tfrac{1}{4}[(a_1 + c_1)\mathbf{i} + (a_2 + b + c_2)\mathbf{j} + a_3\mathbf{k}].$$

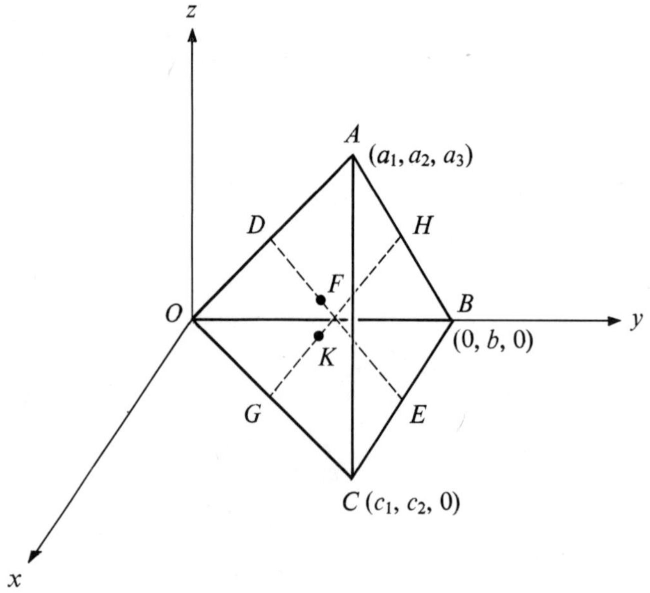

Figure 2.11

Next, let G be the midpoint of OC and H the midpoint of AB. It may be shown as above that

$$GH = \tfrac{1}{2}[(a_1 - c_1)\mathbf{i} + (a_2 + b - c_2)\mathbf{j} + a_3\mathbf{k}].$$

Therefore if K is the midpoint of GH, then

$$\begin{aligned}\mathbf{OK} &= \mathbf{OG} + \mathbf{GK} = \tfrac{1}{2}(\mathbf{DC} + \mathbf{GH})\\ &= \tfrac{1}{4}[(a_1 + c_1)\mathbf{i} + (a_2 + b + c_2)\mathbf{j} + a_3\mathbf{k}].\end{aligned}$$

Since $\mathbf{OF} = \mathbf{OK}$, necessarily $F = K$ and the segments DE and GH intersect at their midpoints. Since DE and GH are any two of the segments joining midpoints of opposite sides, this proves that all three segments meet in a common point of bisection.

EXERCISES

In each of Exercises 1–6 express the vector $\mathbf{AB}$ in terms of the basis $\{\mathbf{i}, \mathbf{j}\}$ or $\{\mathbf{i}, \mathbf{j}, \mathbf{k}\}$, whichever is applicable.

1. $A = (3, -7)$, $B = (0, 5)$ [i.e., A has coordinates $(3, -7)$ and B has coordinates $(0, 5)$].
2. $A = (4, -1, 2)$, $B = (7, -3, -3)$.
3. $A = (0, -1)$, $B = (-1, 0)$.
4. $A = (3, -9, -3)$, $B = (4, 2, -8)$.
5. $A = (7, 7, -7)$, $B = (3, -4, 5)$.
6. $A = (1, 9)$, $B = (-7, 3)$.
7. If a triangle has two medians of the same length, then show that the triangle is isosceles.
8. If the vector $\mathbf{x} = 2\mathbf{i} - \mathbf{j} + \mathbf{k} \in V_3$ has initial point $(-7, 3, -5)$, then find $a \in \mathsf{R}$ so that the terminal point of the vector $a\mathbf{x}$ lies in the xy-plane. Find $b \in \mathsf{R}$ so that the terminal point of $b\mathbf{x}$ lies in the xz-plane. Find $c \in \mathsf{R}$ so that the terminal point of $c\mathbf{x}$ lies in the yz-plane.
9. If points A and B have respective coordinates (a_1, a_2, a_3) and (b_1, b_2, b_3), then find the coordinates of the point P on the segment AB such that $d(A, P)/d(A, B) = r$, where $0 < r < 1$.

10. Does the line through the two points with coordinates $(2, -1, -3)$ and $(-6, 3, 9)$ pass through the origin?
11. Find conditions under which the line passing through the two points with coordinates (a_1, a_2, a_3) and (b_1, b_2, b_3) also passes through the origin.
12. Let V and W be finite-dimensional vector spaces and let $V \xrightarrow{f} W$ be a homomorphism such that $\operatorname{im} f = W$. Prove that $\dim V \geq \dim W$.
13. Prove that a homomorphism $V \xrightarrow{f} W$ maps each subspace of V into a subspace of W. If S is a subspace of W and $T = \{\mathbf{x} \in V \mid f(\mathbf{x}) \in S\}$, then prove that T is a subspace of V.
14. If $V \xrightarrow{f} W$ is a homomorphism, then define the *kernel* of f by $\ker f = \{\mathbf{x} \in V \mid f(\mathbf{x}) = \mathbf{0}\}$. Prove that $\ker f$ is a subspace of V. If $\operatorname{im} f = W$, then prove that $\dim V = \dim W + \dim \ker f$. Prove that f is an isomorphism if and only if $\ker f = \{\mathbf{0}\}$.

Chapter Three

Inner Product Spaces

1. INNER PRODUCTS

Two nonzero vectors **x** and **y** in either V_2 or V_3 have a well-defined least angle Θ between them, as indicated in Fig. 3.1. We always have

$$0 \leq \Theta \leq \pi,$$

with $\Theta = 0$ if $\mathbf{y} = a\mathbf{x}$ for some $a > 0$, and $\Theta = \pi$ if $\mathbf{y} = a\mathbf{x}$ for some $a < 0$.

A useful operation in either V_2 or V_3 is the *dot product* defined below. If $\mathbf{x}, \mathbf{y} \in V_2$ (or V_3), then the dot product of **x** and **y** is a scalar denoted by $\mathbf{x} \cdot \mathbf{y}$ and defined by

3.1 $$\mathbf{x} \cdot \mathbf{y} = |\mathbf{x}|\,|\mathbf{y}| \cos \Theta,$$

where Θ is the angle between **x** and **y**. We recall that $|\mathbf{x}|$ denotes the length of vector **x**. The angle Θ may be taken to be any angle if $\mathbf{x} = \mathbf{0}$ or $\mathbf{y} = \mathbf{0}$, in which case we have, by 3.1,

$$\mathbf{x} \cdot \mathbf{y} = 0 \text{ if } \mathbf{x} = \mathbf{0} \text{ or } \mathbf{y} = \mathbf{0}.$$

Example 1. If vectors **AB** and **AC** are as given in Fig. 3.2, then find $\mathbf{AB} \cdot \mathbf{AC}$.

Solution: By 3.1,

$$\begin{aligned} \mathbf{AB} \cdot \mathbf{AC} &= |\mathbf{AB}|\,|\mathbf{AC}| \cos \pi/3 \\ &= 3 \cdot 4 \cdot \tfrac{1}{2}, \text{ or } 6. \end{aligned}$$

There is only one angle Θ between 0 and π for which $\cos \Theta = 0$, namely the right angle $\Theta = \pi/2$. This fact allows us to state the following result.

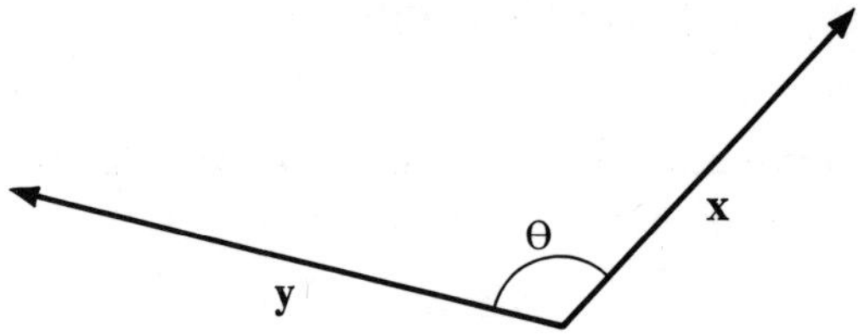

Figure 3.1

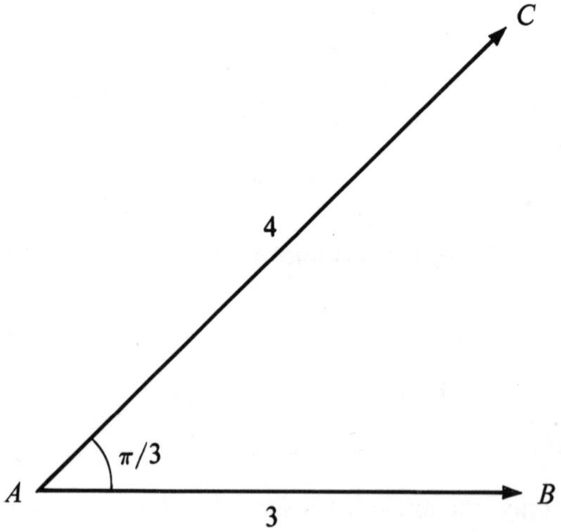

Figure 3.2

3.2. THEOREM. Two nonzero vectors $\mathbf{x}$ and $\mathbf{y}$ in V_2 or V_3 are perpendicular if and only if $\mathbf{x}\cdot\mathbf{y} = 0$.

An operation such as the dot product, which associates with each pair of vectors $(\mathbf{x}, \mathbf{y})$ a unique scalar $\mathbf{x}\cdot\mathbf{y}$, is called an *inner product* if it has the following properties.

3.3. DEFINITION OF AN INNER PRODUCT. An operation which associates with each pair of vectors $(\mathbf{x}, \mathbf{y})$ of a vector space V a unique scalar $\mathbf{x}\cdot\mathbf{y}$ is defined to be an inner product if and only if it has the following three properties. For all $\mathbf{x}, \mathbf{y}, \mathbf{z} \in V$ and $a \in \mathsf{R}$:

(1) $\mathbf{x}\cdot(\mathbf{y} + \mathbf{z}) = \mathbf{x}\cdot\mathbf{y} + \mathbf{x}\cdot\mathbf{z}, \quad (\mathbf{y} + \mathbf{z})\cdot\mathbf{x} = \mathbf{y}\cdot\mathbf{x} + \mathbf{z}\cdot\mathbf{x},$

(2) $(a\mathbf{x})\cdot\mathbf{y} = a(\mathbf{x}\cdot\mathbf{y}),$

(3) $\mathbf{x}\cdot\mathbf{x} \geq 0$, with $\mathbf{x}\cdot\mathbf{x} = 0$ if and only if $\mathbf{x} = \mathbf{0}$.

A vector space having an inner product is called an *inner product space*.

If we let $\mathbf{y} = \mathbf{z} = \mathbf{0}$ in (1) above and use the fact that $0 + \mathbf{x}\cdot\mathbf{0} = \mathbf{x}\cdot\mathbf{0}$, then we get

$$0 + \mathbf{x}\cdot\mathbf{0} = \mathbf{x}\cdot\mathbf{0} = \mathbf{x}\cdot(\mathbf{0} + \mathbf{0}) = \mathbf{x}\cdot\mathbf{0} + \mathbf{x}\cdot\mathbf{0}.$$

Hence, using the cancellation law in R, we get $0 = \mathbf{x}\cdot\mathbf{0}$. We state this property thus:

$$\mathbf{x}\cdot\mathbf{0} = \mathbf{0}\cdot\mathbf{x} = 0 \text{ for all } \mathbf{x} \in V.$$

An inner product space V is called a *Euclidean space* if and only if it has the following additional commutative property:

3.4 $$\mathbf{x}\cdot\mathbf{y} = \mathbf{y}\cdot\mathbf{x} \text{ for all } \mathbf{x}, \mathbf{y} \in V.$$

In a Euclidean space V we can extend 3.3(2) as follows: $\mathbf{x}\cdot(a\mathbf{y}) = (a\mathbf{y})\cdot\mathbf{x} = a(\mathbf{y}\cdot\mathbf{x}) = a(\mathbf{x}\cdot\mathbf{y})$. That is,

3.5 $$\mathbf{x}\cdot(a\mathbf{y}) = a(\mathbf{x}\cdot\mathbf{y}) \text{ for all } \mathbf{x}, \mathbf{y} \in V,\ a \in \mathsf{R}.$$

The dot product in V_2 and V_3 defined by 3.1 actually makes V_2 and V_3 into Euclidean spaces, as we shall presently show. We note that

$$\mathbf{x}\cdot\mathbf{x} = |\mathbf{x}|\,|\mathbf{x}| \cos 0 = |\mathbf{x}|^2$$

for all $\mathbf{x}$ in V_2 or V_3. This suggests that we define the length of a vector in any Euclidean space V as follows.

3.6. DEFINITION OF LENGTH. The length of each vector $\mathbf{x}$ in a Euclidean space V is denoted by $|\mathbf{x}|$ and defined by

$$|\mathbf{x}| = \sqrt{\mathbf{x}\cdot\mathbf{x}}.$$

By 3.3(3),

$$|\mathbf{x}| = 0 \text{ if and only if } \mathbf{x} = \mathbf{0}.$$

By 3.3(2) and 3.5,

$$(a\mathbf{x})\cdot(a\mathbf{x}) = a[\mathbf{x}\cdot(a\mathbf{x})] = a[a(\mathbf{x}\cdot\mathbf{x})] = a^2(\mathbf{x}\cdot\mathbf{x})$$

and therefore

3.7 $$|a\mathbf{x}| = |a|\,|\mathbf{x}| \text{ for all } \mathbf{x} \in V,\ a \in \mathsf{R}.$$

We recall that $\sqrt{a^2} = |a|$, the absolute value of a.

A vector of length 1 is called a *unit vector* or a *normal vector*. Some scalar multiple of every nonzero vector is a unit vector:

$$\text{if } |\mathbf{x}| = b \neq 0, \text{ then } \left|\frac{1}{b}\mathbf{x}\right| = 1$$

by 3.7. The vectors $\mathbf{i}$, $\mathbf{j}$, and $\mathbf{k}$ of V_3 are examples of unit vectors.

Using 3.3(1) and (2) and 3.5, we easily show that

3.8 $$\left(\sum_{i=1}^{m} a_i\mathbf{x}_i\right)\cdot\left(\sum_{j=1}^{n} b_j\mathbf{y}_j\right) = \sum_{i=1}^{m}\sum_{j=1}^{n} a_ib_j(\mathbf{x}_i\cdot\mathbf{y}_j)$$

for all $a_1, \cdots, a_m, b_1, \cdots, b_n \in \mathsf{R}$ and $\mathbf{x}_1, \cdots, \mathbf{x}_m, \mathbf{y}_1, \cdots, \mathbf{y}_n \in V$, a Euclidean space.

A useful property of a Euclidean space is as follows.

3.9. CAUCHY'S INEQUALITY. If V is a Euclidean space, then

$$|\mathbf{x}\cdot\mathbf{y}| \leq |\mathbf{x}|\,|\mathbf{y}| \text{ for all } \mathbf{x}, \mathbf{y} \in V.$$

Proof: We observe that $|\mathbf{x}\cdot\mathbf{y}|$ denotes the absolute value of the scalar $\mathbf{x}\cdot\mathbf{y}$, whereas $|\mathbf{x}|$ and $|\mathbf{y}|$ denote lengths of vectors. If $\mathbf{x} = \mathbf{0}$, then $\mathbf{x}\cdot\mathbf{y} = 0$ and Cauchy's inequality is true ($0 \leq 0$). So let us assume that $\mathbf{x} \neq \mathbf{0}$. For convenience, let

$$a = \mathbf{x}\cdot\mathbf{x}, \quad b = \mathbf{x}\cdot\mathbf{y}, \quad \text{and} \quad \mathbf{z} = a\mathbf{y} - b\mathbf{x}.$$

Then, by 3.4 and 3.8,

$$\begin{aligned}\mathbf{z}\cdot\mathbf{z} &= (a\mathbf{y})\cdot(a\mathbf{y}) - 2(a\mathbf{y})\cdot(b\mathbf{x}) + (b\mathbf{x})\cdot(b\mathbf{x}) \\ &= a^2(\mathbf{y}\cdot\mathbf{y}) - 2ab^2 + b^2a \\ &= a[a(\mathbf{y}\cdot\mathbf{y}) - b^2].\end{aligned}$$

Since $\mathbf{z}\cdot\mathbf{z} \geq 0$ and $a > 0$, we have $a(\mathbf{y}\cdot\mathbf{y}) - b^2 \geq 0$ and $b^2 \leq a(\mathbf{y}\cdot\mathbf{y})$, i.e.,

$$(\mathbf{x}\cdot\mathbf{y})^2 \leq (\mathbf{x}\cdot\mathbf{x})(\mathbf{y}\cdot\mathbf{y}).$$

Taking square roots, we obtain Cauchy's inequality.

A dot product may be defined in the vector space R_n as follows. For all $(a_1, a_2, \cdots, a_n), (b_1, b_2, \cdots, b_n) \in \mathsf{R}_n$, define

3.10 $$(a_1, a_2, \cdots, a_n)\cdot(b_1, b_2, \cdots, b_n) = a_1b_1 + a_2b_2 + \cdots + a_nb_n.$$

Thus the dot product of two vectors of R_n is a scalar.

We easily verify that the dot product (3.10) makes R_n into a Euclidean space. Thus if $\mathbf{x}, \mathbf{y}, \mathbf{z} \in \mathsf{R}_n$ are given by

$$\mathbf{x} = (a_1, a_2, \cdots, a_n), \quad \mathbf{y} = (b_1, b_2, \cdots, b_n), \quad \mathbf{z} = (c_1, c_2, \cdots, c_n),$$

then we have

$$\begin{aligned}(\mathbf{x} + \mathbf{y})\cdot\mathbf{z} &= (a_1 + b_1, a_2 + b_2, \cdots, a_n + b_n)\cdot(c_1, c_2, \cdots, c_n) \\ &= (a_1 + b_1)c_1 + (a_2 + b_2)c_2 + \cdots + (a_n + b_n)c_n \\ &= (a_1c_1 + a_2c_2 + \cdots + a_nc_n) + (b_1c_1 + b_2c_2 + \cdots + b_nc_n) \\ &= \mathbf{x}\cdot\mathbf{z} + \mathbf{y}\cdot\mathbf{z}.\end{aligned}$$

The proof that $\mathbf{z}\cdot(\mathbf{x} + \mathbf{y}) = \mathbf{z}\cdot\mathbf{x} + \mathbf{z}\cdot\mathbf{y}$ is similar. If $r \in \mathsf{R}$, then

$$\begin{aligned}(r\mathbf{x})\cdot\mathbf{y} &= (ra_1, ra_2, \cdots, ra_n)\cdot(b_1, b_2, \cdots, b_n) \\ &= (ra_1)b_1 + (ra_2)b_2 + \cdots + (ra_n)b_n \\ &= r(a_1b_1 + a_2b_2 + \cdots + a_nb_n) \\ &= r(\mathbf{x}\cdot\mathbf{y}).\end{aligned}$$

Since

$$\mathbf{x}\cdot\mathbf{x} = a_1^2 + a_2^2 + \cdots + a_n^2,$$

evidently $\mathbf{x}\cdot\mathbf{x} \geq 0$. Also, $\mathbf{x}\cdot\mathbf{x} = 0$ if and only if $a_1 = a_2 = \cdots = a_n = 0$, i.e., $\mathbf{x} = \mathbf{0}$. Finally,

$$\mathbf{x}\cdot\mathbf{y} = a_1b_1 + a_2b_2 + \cdots + a_nb_n = b_1a_1 + b_2a_2 + \cdots + b_na_n = \mathbf{y}\cdot\mathbf{x}.$$

Therefore we have proved the following result.

3.11. THEOREM. The vector space R_n, with inner product defined by 3.10, is a Euclidean space.

According to 3.6, the length of a vector in R_n is given by

$$|(a_1, a_2, \cdots, a_n)| = \sqrt{a_1^2 + a_2^2 + \cdots + a_n^2}.$$

Thus it is clear that each of the vectors $\mathbf{u}_1, \mathbf{u}_2, \cdots, \mathbf{u}_n$ defined on page 19 is a unit vector. Another unit vector is

$$\left(\frac{e_1}{\sqrt{n}}, \frac{e_2}{\sqrt{n}}, \cdots, \frac{e_n}{\sqrt{n}}\right),$$

where each e_i is either 1 or -1.

We recall from Chapter Two that the mappings

$$V_2 \xrightarrow{f} \mathsf{R}_2,\ f(\mathbf{x}) = (c_1, c_2), \text{ the components of } \mathbf{x},$$

$$V_3 \xrightarrow{f} \mathsf{R}_3,\ f(\mathbf{x}) = (c_1, c_2, c_3), \text{ the components of } \mathbf{x},$$

are isomorphisms. Let us show that each f preserves dot products, i.e., that

(3.12) $$\mathbf{x}\cdot\mathbf{y} = f(\mathbf{x})\cdot f(\mathbf{y}) \text{ for all } \mathbf{x}, \mathbf{y} \in V_2 \text{ (or } V_3).$$

The proof of 3.12 for V_2 given below extends almost verbatim to V_3.

Proof of 3.12: If either $\mathbf{x} = \mathbf{0}$ or $\mathbf{y} = \mathbf{0}$, then $\mathbf{x}\cdot\mathbf{y} = f(\mathbf{x})\cdot f(\mathbf{y}) = 0$. If $\mathbf{x} \neq \mathbf{0}$ and $\mathbf{y} \neq \mathbf{0}$, then let $\mathbf{x}$ and $\mathbf{y}$ be position vectors (Fig. 3.3), Θ the angle between them, and P and Q be the terminal points of $\mathbf{x}$ and $\mathbf{y}$, respectively. By the law of cosines, the distance between P and Q is given by

$$[d(P, Q)]^2 = |\mathbf{x}|^2 + |\mathbf{y}|^2 - 2|\mathbf{x}|\,|\mathbf{y}| \cos \Theta.$$

Hence, in view of the definition of the dot product in V_2(3.1),

$$[d(P, Q)]^2 = |\mathbf{x}|^2 + |\mathbf{y}|^2 - 2(\mathbf{x}\cdot\mathbf{y}).$$

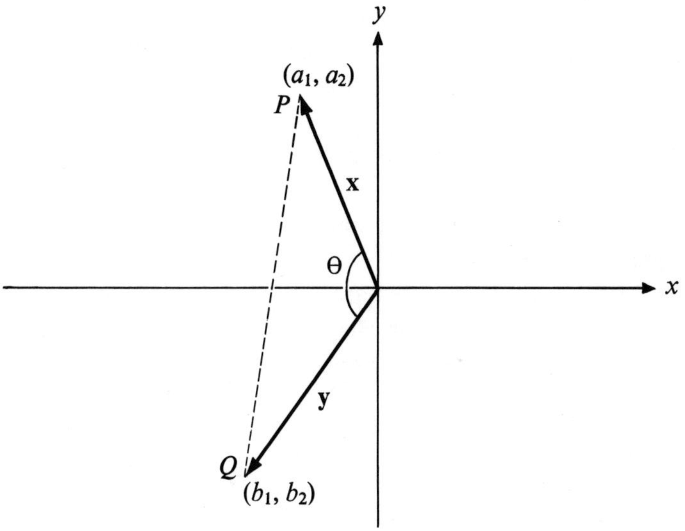

Figure 3.3

Using the distance formula, we have

$$(a_1 - b_1)^2 + (a_2 - b_2)^2 = (a_1{}^2 + a_2{}^2) + (b_1{}^2 + b_2{}^2) - 2(\mathbf{x}\cdot\mathbf{y}),$$

which reduces to

$$-2a_1b_1 - 2a_2b_2 = -2(\mathbf{x}\cdot\mathbf{y})$$

or

$$\mathbf{x}\cdot\mathbf{y} = a_1b_1 + a_2b_2.$$

Since $f(\mathbf{x}) = (a_1, a_2)$, $f(\mathbf{y}) = (b_1, b_2)$, and $f(\mathbf{x})\cdot f(\mathbf{y}) = a_1b_1 + a_2b_2$ by 3.10, we have proved 3.12.

The isomorphism between V_2 and R_2 and between V_3 and R_3 preserves dot products by 3.12. Therefore, since R_2 and R_3 are Euclidean, the dot product in V_2 and V_3 is actually an inner product with property 3.4. This proves the following result.

3.13. THEOREM. The vector spaces V_2 and V_3 are Euclidean.

Example 2. Under what conditions are the diagonals of a parallelogram perpendicular?

Solution: If $\mathbf{x}$ and $\mathbf{y}$ are the nonparallel sides of the parallelogram, then $\mathbf{x} + \mathbf{y}$ and $\mathbf{x} - \mathbf{y}$ are its diagonals (Fig. 3.4). By 3.2, $\mathbf{x} + \mathbf{y}$ and $\mathbf{x} - \mathbf{y}$ are perpendicular if and only if

$$(\mathbf{x} + \mathbf{y})\cdot(\mathbf{x} - \mathbf{y}) = 0.$$

Since V_2 is Euclidean, we have $\mathbf{x}\cdot\mathbf{y} = \mathbf{y}\cdot\mathbf{x}$ and

$$(\mathbf{x} + \mathbf{y})\cdot(\mathbf{x} - \mathbf{y}) = \mathbf{x}\cdot\mathbf{x} - \mathbf{y}\cdot\mathbf{y}.$$

Hence $\mathbf{x} + \mathbf{y}$ and $\mathbf{x} - \mathbf{y}$ are perpendicular if and only if $\mathbf{x}\cdot\mathbf{x} = \mathbf{y}\cdot\mathbf{y}$, or

$$|\mathbf{x}| = |\mathbf{y}|,$$

i.e., if and only if the parallelogram is equilateral. One instance of an equilateral parallelogram is a square.

Example 3. Prove that the line joining the midpoints of opposite sides of a regular tetrahedron is perpendicular to these sides.

Solution: Let A, B, C, and D be the vertices of a regular tetrahedron (Fig. 3.5). Thus, by assumption, each face of the tetrahedron is

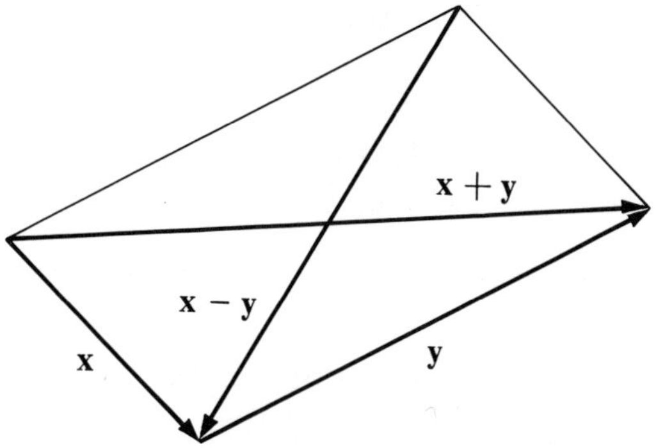

Figure 3.4

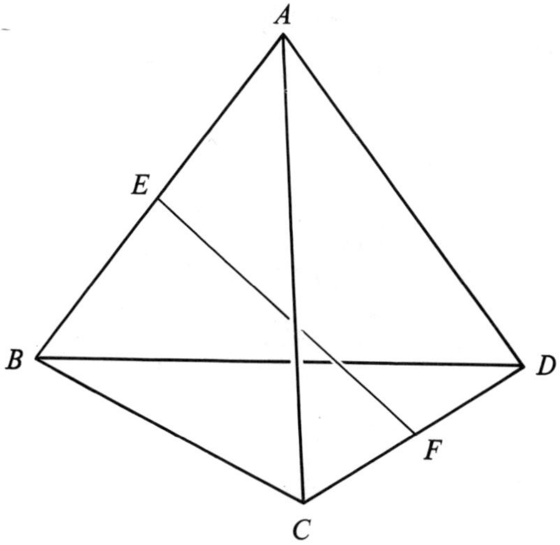

Figure 3.5

an equilateral triangle. Let E be the midpoint of AB and F the midpoint of CD. We wish to prove that **AB** and **EF** are perpendicular, i.e., that

$$\mathbf{AB}\cdot\mathbf{EF} = 0.$$

We leave it as an exercise for you to prove that

$$\mathbf{EF} = \tfrac{1}{2}(\mathbf{AD} + \mathbf{BC})$$

in any tetrahedron. Hence

$$\begin{aligned}\mathbf{AB}\cdot\mathbf{EF} &= \tfrac{1}{2}(\mathbf{AB}\cdot\mathbf{AD} + \mathbf{AB}\cdot\mathbf{BC})\\ &= \tfrac{1}{2}(\mathbf{AB}\cdot\mathbf{AD} - \mathbf{BA}\cdot\mathbf{BC}).\end{aligned}$$

However, since the angles between **AB** and **AD** and between **BA** and **BC** are equal and since

$$|\mathbf{AB}| = |\mathbf{AD}| = |\mathbf{BA}| = |\mathbf{BC}|,$$

evidently

$$\mathbf{AB}\cdot\mathbf{AD} = \mathbf{BA}\cdot\mathbf{BC}.$$

Hence $\mathbf{AB}\cdot\mathbf{EF} = 0$, as we wished to show.

Example 4. If points A, B, and C have coordinates $(1, 1, 1)$, $(4, 1, 4)$, and $(0, 5, 8)$, respectively, then is ABC a right triangle?

Solution: The vectors **AB**, **BC**, and **AC** have respective components $(3, 0, 3)$, $(-4, 4, 4)$, and $(-1, 4, 7)$. Since

$$(3, 0, 3)\cdot(-4, 4, 4) = -12 + 12 = 0,$$

$\mathbf{AB}\cdot\mathbf{BC} = 0$ and therefore **AB** and **BC** are perpendicular by 3.2. Hence ABC is a right triangle.

Example 5. Find the angles of the triangle ABC of Fig. 3.6.

Solution: The components of **AB** are $(1 - (-3), 2 - 1)$ and the components of **AC** are $(1 - (-3), -2 - 1)$. Hence

$$\mathbf{AB} = 4\mathbf{i} + \mathbf{j}, \quad |\mathbf{AB}| = \sqrt{17}, \quad \mathbf{AC} = 4\mathbf{i} - 3\mathbf{j}, \quad |\mathbf{AC}| = 5,$$

and by 3.1 and 3.12

$$\mathbf{AB}\cdot\mathbf{AC} = \sqrt{17}\cdot 5\cdot\cos\theta_1 = (4, 1)\cdot(4, -3) = 4\cdot 4 + 1\cdot(-3) = 13.$$

Therefore

$$\cos\theta_1 = \frac{13}{5\sqrt{17}} = \frac{13}{85}\sqrt{17}, \text{ or } .6306 \text{ approx.}$$

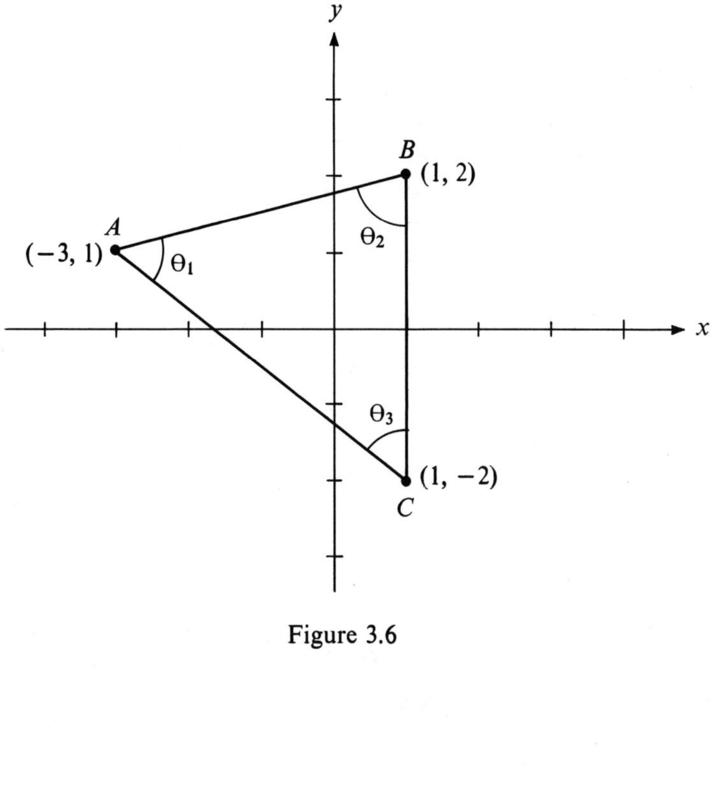

Figure 3.6

From a table of trigonometric functions,

$$\theta_1 = 50°54' \text{ approx.}$$

Similarly,

$$\mathbf{BA} = -4\mathbf{i} - \mathbf{j}, \quad |\mathbf{BA}| = \sqrt{17}, \quad \mathbf{BC} = -4\mathbf{j}, \quad |\mathbf{BC}| = 4, \quad \text{and}$$

$$\mathbf{BA}\cdot\mathbf{BC} = 4\sqrt{17}\cos\theta_2 = (-4, -1)\cdot(0, -4) = 4.$$

Therefore

$$\cos\theta_2 = \frac{\sqrt{17}}{17} = .2425 \text{ approx.}$$

and

$$\theta_2 = 75°58' \text{ approx.}$$

Finally,

$$\mathbf{CB} = 4\mathbf{j}, \quad \mathbf{CA} = -4\mathbf{i} + 3\mathbf{j},$$

and

$$\mathbf{CB}\cdot\mathbf{CA} = 4\cdot5\cdot\cos\theta_3 = (0, 4)\cdot(-4, 3) = 12.$$

Hence

$$\cos\theta_3 = .6$$

and

$$\theta_3 = 53°8' \text{ approx.}$$

We check our work by noting that

$$\theta_1 + \theta_2 + \theta_3 = 180.$$

Of course, having found θ_1 and θ_2, we could have obtained θ_3 from the equation above.

The angles of a triangle in E_3 can be found in exactly the same way.

EXERCISES

In each of Exercises 1–8 tell whether or not the points with given coordinates are the vertices of a right triangle.

1. $(3, 0, 1), (5, -2, 2), (5, -1, 4)$.
2. $(0, 3), (-2, -12), (-4, 11)$.
3. $(-3, 1), (5, 4), (0, -7)$.
4. $(1, 1), (-1, -1), (-3, 7)$.
5. $(2, 3, 1), (1, 0, 3), (0, 2, 1)$.

6. (1, 1, 1), (−1, 2, 2), (3, −5, 4).
7. (2, 5, 1), (−1, −4, −2), (3, −6, 0).
8. (2, 5, −2), (4, 5, −1), (1, 3, 0).

In each of Exercises 9–12 find a unit vector which is perpendicular to the two given vectors of V_3.

9. $\mathbf{i} - \mathbf{j}, \mathbf{i} + \mathbf{j}$.
10. $\mathbf{i} + 2\mathbf{j} - \mathbf{k}, 3\mathbf{i} - \mathbf{j}$.
11. $\mathbf{i} + \mathbf{j} + \mathbf{k}, \mathbf{i} - \mathbf{j} - \mathbf{k}$.
12. $3\mathbf{i} - \mathbf{j}, \mathbf{j} - 2\mathbf{k}$.

In each of Exercises 13–16 find the angles of the triangle whose vertices have the given coordinates.

13. (5, 7), (−5, −3), (4, 6).
14. (4, 2), (1, 0), (−3, −6).
15. (1, 0, 0), (0, 2, 0), (0, 0, 3).
16. (1, −1, 1), (−1, 1, 1), (1, 1, −1).
17. In a regular tetrahedron, prove vectorially that the line drawn from each vertex to the centroid of the opposite base is perpendicular to each median of that base.
18. If A, B, C, and D are the vertices of a regular tetrahedron, then prove that $\mathbf{AB} \cdot \mathbf{CD} = 0$.
19. Interpret Cauchy's inequality in the vector space R_n.
20. Prove that the perpendiculars drawn from the vertices of a triangle to the opposite sides meet in a point.
21. Prove that the perpendicular bisectors of the sides of a triangle meet in a point.
22. Is the converse of Example 3, page 58, true? That is, if the three lines joining the midpoints of opposite sides of a terahedron are perpendicular to these sides, is the terahedron regular?

2. NORMAL ORTHOGONAL BASES

We recall that two nonzero vectors in V_2 or V_3 are perpendicular if and only if their dot product is zero. This leads us to say that two nonzero vectors in any Euclidean space V are *orthogonal* (a synonym for perpendicular) if and only if their inner product is zero.

3.14. DEFINITION OF A NORMAL ORTHOGONAL BASIS. Let V be a finite-dimensional Euclidean space. A basis $\mathbf{x}_1, \mathbf{x}_2, \cdots, \mathbf{x}_n$ of V is called a normal orthogonal basis if and only if

(1) $$|\mathbf{x}_i| = 1, \qquad i = 1, 2, \cdots, n,$$

and

(2) $$\mathbf{x}_i \cdot \mathbf{x}_j = 0 \text{ if } i \neq j,\ i, j = 1, 2, \cdots, n.$$

The basis $\{\mathbf{i}, \mathbf{j}, \mathbf{k}\}$ is a normal orthogonal basis of V_3, since

$$|\mathbf{i}| = |\mathbf{j}| = |\mathbf{k}| = 1, \quad \mathbf{i}\cdot\mathbf{j} = \mathbf{i}\cdot\mathbf{k} = \mathbf{j}\cdot\mathbf{k} = 0.$$

As another example, the basis $\{\mathbf{u}_1, \mathbf{u}_2, \cdots, \mathbf{u}_n\}$ of R_n defined on page 19 is a normal orthogonal basis. Thus

$$|\mathbf{u}_i| = 1, \quad \mathbf{u}_i \cdot \mathbf{u}_j = 0 \text{ if } i \neq j,\ i, j = 1, 2, \cdots, n.$$

That every finite-dimensional Euclidean space has a normal orthogonal basis is proved below.

3.15. THEOREM. Every finite-dimensional Euclidean space V has a normal orthogonal basis.

Proof: If $\dim V = 1$, then any set $\{\mathbf{x}\}$ with $|\mathbf{x}| = 1$ is a normal orthogonal basis. Assume that $\dim V = n, n > 1$, and that every Euclidean space of dimension $n - 1$ has a normal orthogonal basis. Let $\mathbf{x}_1$ be any unit vector of V and

$$S = \{\mathbf{y} \in V \mid \mathbf{x}_1 \cdot \mathbf{y} = 0\}.$$

If $\mathbf{y}_1, \mathbf{y}_2 \in S$, $a \in \mathsf{R}$, then $\mathbf{x}_1 \cdot \mathbf{y}_1 = \mathbf{x}_1 \cdot \mathbf{y}_2 = 0$ and

$$\mathbf{x}_1 \cdot (\mathbf{y}_1 + \mathbf{y}_2) = \mathbf{x}_1 \cdot \mathbf{y}_1 + \mathbf{x}_1 \cdot \mathbf{y}_2 = 0, \quad \mathbf{x}_1 \cdot (a\mathbf{y}_1) = a(\mathbf{x}_1 \cdot \mathbf{y}_1) = 0.$$

Thus $\mathbf{y}_1 + \mathbf{y}_2$ and $a\mathbf{y}_1$ are in S, and we conclude that S is a subspace of V. Since $\mathbf{x}_1 \cdot a\mathbf{x}_1 = a(\mathbf{x}_1 \cdot \mathbf{x}_1) = a$, $\mathbf{x}_1 \cdot a\mathbf{x}_1 = 0$ if and only if $a = 0$. This proves that

$$S \cap \mathsf{R}\mathbf{x}_1 = \{\mathbf{0}\}.$$

For each $\mathbf{z} \in V$, $\mathbf{x}_1 \cdot \mathbf{z} = b$, a scalar, and

$$\mathbf{x}_1 \cdot (\mathbf{z} - b\mathbf{x}_1) = \mathbf{x}_1 \cdot \mathbf{z} - b(\mathbf{x}_1 \cdot \mathbf{x}_1) = b - b = 0.$$

Hence $\mathbf{z} - b\mathbf{x}_1 \in S$ and $\mathbf{z} \in S + \mathsf{R}\mathbf{x}_1$. This proves that

$$S + \mathsf{R}\mathbf{x}_1 = V.$$

Since a basis of S together with $\mathbf{x}_1$ forms a basis of V, evidently

$$\dim S = n - 1.$$

Thus S is a Euclidean space of dimension $n - 1$, which by assumption has a normal orthogonal basis, say $\{\mathbf{x}_2, \mathbf{x}_3, \cdots, \mathbf{x}_n\}$. Since

$$|\mathbf{x}_1| = 1, \quad |\mathbf{x}_i| = 1 \text{ if } i = 2, 3, \cdots, n,$$

and

$$\mathbf{x}_1 \cdot \mathbf{x}_i = 0 \text{ if } i = 2, 3, \cdots, n,$$
$$\mathbf{x}_i \cdot \mathbf{x}_j = 0 \text{ if } i \neq j,\ i, j = 2, 3, \cdots, n,$$

clearly $\{\mathbf{x}_1, \mathbf{x}_2, \mathbf{x}_3, \cdots, \mathbf{x}_n\}$ is a normal orthogonal basis of V. The theorem now follows by mathematical induction.

Another way of interpreting 3.15 is that for any two n-dimensional Euclidean spaces V and W there exists an isomorphism $V \xrightarrow{f} W$ which also preserves inner products. For if V and W have normal orthogonal bases $\{\mathbf{v}_1, \mathbf{v}_2, \cdots, \mathbf{v}_n\}$ and $\{\mathbf{w}_1, \mathbf{w}_2, \cdots, \mathbf{w}_n\}$ respectively, then the mapping

$$V \xrightarrow{f} W, \quad f\left(\sum_{i=1}^{n} a_i\mathbf{v}_i\right) = \sum_{i=1}^{n} a_i\mathbf{w}_i, \qquad a_i \in \mathsf{R},$$

is an isomorphism which preserves inner products:

$$\left(\sum_{i=1}^{n} a_i\mathbf{v}_i\right) \cdot \left(\sum_{j=1}^{n} b_j\mathbf{v}_j\right) = \sum_{i=1}^{n} a_ib_i = \left(\sum_{i=1}^{n} a_i\mathbf{w}_i\right) \cdot \left(\sum_{j=1}^{n} b_j\mathbf{w}_j\right).$$

On the other hand, if we know that for every pair of n-dimensional Euclidean spaces there exists an isomorphism which preserves inner products, then we know immediately that every n-dimensional Euclidean space V has a normal orthogonal basis. Thus R_n has a normal orthogonal basis $\{\mathbf{u}_1, \mathbf{u}_2, \cdots, \mathbf{u}_n\}$, and an isomorphism $\mathsf{R}_n \xrightarrow{f} V$ which preserves inner products maps $\{\mathbf{u}_1, \mathbf{u}_2, \cdots, \mathbf{u}_n\}$ into a normal orthogonal basis $\{f(\mathbf{u}_1), f(\mathbf{u}_2), \cdots, f(\mathbf{u}_n)\}$ of V.

EXERCISES

In each of the following exercises V is assumed to be a finite-dimensional Euclidean space.

1. For each subspace A of V, let $A' = \{\mathbf{x} \in V \mid \mathbf{x} \cdot \mathbf{y} = 0 \text{ for all } \mathbf{y} \in A\}$. Prove that A' is a subspace of V and that

$$A + A' = V, \quad A \cap A' = \{\mathbf{0}\}.$$

2. Prove the *triangle inequality*

$$|\mathbf{x} + \mathbf{y}| \leq |\mathbf{x}| + |\mathbf{y}| \text{ for all } \mathbf{x}, \mathbf{y} \in V.$$

3. Under what conditions on $\mathbf{x}, \mathbf{y} \in V$ is $|\mathbf{x} \cdot \mathbf{y}| = |\mathbf{x}|\,|\mathbf{y}|$?
4. Does the following cancellation law hold in V? If $\mathbf{x} \cdot \mathbf{z} = \mathbf{y} \cdot \mathbf{z} \neq 0$, then $\mathbf{x} = \mathbf{y}$.
5. Prove that $\max\{|\mathbf{x}|, |\mathbf{y}|\} \leq \max\{|\mathbf{x} + \mathbf{y}|, |\mathbf{x} - \mathbf{y}|\}$ for all $\mathbf{x}, \mathbf{y} \in V$.
6. Prove that $|r\mathbf{x} + (1 - r)\mathbf{y}| < \max\{|\mathbf{x}|, |\mathbf{y}|\}$ for all $\mathbf{x}, \mathbf{y} \in V$, $r \in \mathsf{R}$, with $0 < r < 1$.
7. If $\mathbf{x}$ and $\mathbf{y}$ are unit vectors of V_2 or V_3, then prove that the vector $\mathbf{x} + \mathbf{y}$ bisects the angle between $\mathbf{x}$ and $\mathbf{y}$.
8. If (a_1, a_2, a_3) and (b_1, b_2, b_3) are linearly independent vectors of R_3, then find a unit vector $\mathbf{u}$ which is orthogonal to both. Is $\mathbf{u}$ unique?

Chapter Four

Vector Algebras

1. TWO-DIMENSIONAL ALGEBRA

About 1800 Wessel, Argand, and other mathematicians discovered a useful way of multiplying vectors in V_2. This multiplication, called the cross product, was defined relative to a rectangular coordinate system, as shown in Fig. 4.1. Thus the cross product, $\mathbf{u} \times \mathbf{v}$, of vectors $\mathbf{u}$ and $\mathbf{v}$ is a vector whose length is given by

$$|\mathbf{u} \times \mathbf{v}| = |\mathbf{u}|\,|\mathbf{v}|$$

and whose angle with the positive x-axis is the sum of the angles $\mathbf{u}$ and $\mathbf{v}$ make with this axis. In terms of the basis $\{\mathbf{i}, \mathbf{j}\}$ of V_2, this definition has the following form.

4.1. DEFINITION OF CROSS PRODUCT IN V_2. For all a_i, $b_i \in \mathsf{R}$,

$$(a_1\mathbf{i} + a_2\mathbf{j}) \times (b_1\mathbf{i} + b_2\mathbf{j}) = (a_1b_1 - a_2b_2)\mathbf{i} + (a_1b_2 + a_2b_1)\mathbf{j}.$$

We observe that the cross product of two vectors is a vector, whereas the dot product of two vectors is a scalar. In this respect the cross product is more like the usual multiplication operation.

A vector space V which has a product operation such as defined above is called a *vector algebra* if the product operation has the following two properties:

4.2 $\quad (\mathbf{u} + \mathbf{v}) \times \mathbf{w} = \mathbf{u} \times \mathbf{w} + \mathbf{v} \times \mathbf{w}, \quad \mathbf{w} \times (\mathbf{u} + \mathbf{v}) = \mathbf{w} \times \mathbf{u} + \mathbf{w} \times \mathbf{v}$ for all $\mathbf{u}, \mathbf{v}, \mathbf{w} \in V$.

4.3 $\quad (a\mathbf{u}) \times \mathbf{v} = \mathbf{u} \times (a\mathbf{v}) = a(\mathbf{u} \times \mathbf{v})$ for all $\mathbf{u}, \mathbf{v} \in V$, $a \in \mathsf{R}$.

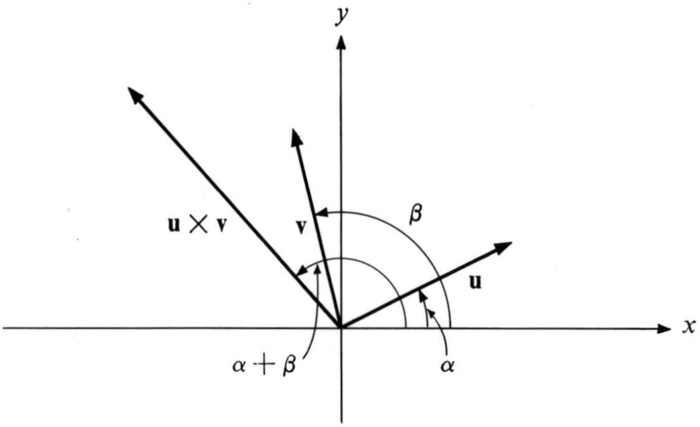

Figure 4.1

It follows from 4.2 that

$$\mathbf{0} \times \mathbf{u} = \mathbf{u} \times \mathbf{0} = \mathbf{0} \text{ for all } \mathbf{u} \in V.$$

$$(-\mathbf{u}) \times \mathbf{v} = \mathbf{u} \times (-\mathbf{v}) = -(\mathbf{u} \times \mathbf{v}) \text{ for all } \mathbf{u}, \mathbf{v} \in V.$$

The cross product in V_2 has properties 4.2 and 4.3. For example, if

$$\mathbf{u} = a_1\mathbf{i} + a_2\mathbf{j}, \quad \mathbf{v} = b_1\mathbf{i} + b_2\mathbf{j}, \quad \text{and} \quad \mathbf{w} = c_1\mathbf{i} + c_2\mathbf{j},$$

then

$$\begin{aligned}(\mathbf{u} + \mathbf{v}) \times \mathbf{w} &= [(a_1 + b_1)\mathbf{i} + (a_2 + b_2)\mathbf{j}] \times (c_1\mathbf{i} + c_2\mathbf{j}) \\ &= [(a_1 + b_1)c_1 - (a_2 + b_2)c_2]\mathbf{i} + [(a_1 + b_1)c_2 \\ &\qquad + (a_2 + b_2)c_1]\mathbf{j} \\ &= [(a_1c_1 - a_2c_2)\mathbf{i} + (a_1c_2 + a_2c_1)\mathbf{j}] + [(b_1c_1 - b_2c_2)\mathbf{i} \\ &\qquad + (b_1c_2 + b_2c_1)\mathbf{j}] \\ &= \mathbf{u} \times \mathbf{w} + \mathbf{v} \times \mathbf{w}.\end{aligned}$$

We prove the other half of 4.2 similarly. The proof of 4.3 proceeds as follows:

$$\begin{aligned}(a\mathbf{u}) \times \mathbf{v} &= (aa_1\mathbf{i} + aa_2\mathbf{j}) \times (b_1\mathbf{i} + b_2\mathbf{j}) \\ &= (aa_1b_1 - aa_2b_2)\mathbf{i} + (aa_1b_2 + aa_2b_1)\mathbf{j} \\ &= a[(a_1b_1 - a_2b_2)\mathbf{i} + (a_1b_2 + a_2b_1)\mathbf{j}] \\ &= a(\mathbf{u} \times \mathbf{v}).\end{aligned}$$

The rest of 4.3 is proved similarly. We conclude that V_2 is a vector algebra.

The cross product in V_2 has many other properties. We shall not carry out the work, but it may easily be shown that:

4.4 $\quad \mathbf{u} \times \mathbf{v} = \mathbf{v} \times \mathbf{u}$ for all $\mathbf{u}, \mathbf{v} \in V_2$.

4.5 $\quad \mathbf{u} \times (\mathbf{v} \times \mathbf{w}) = (\mathbf{u} \times \mathbf{v}) \times \mathbf{w}$ for all $\mathbf{u}, \mathbf{v}, \mathbf{w} \in V_2$.

4.6 $\quad \mathbf{i} \times \mathbf{u} = \mathbf{u} \times \mathbf{i} = \mathbf{u}$ for all $\mathbf{u} \in V_2$.

4.7 Every $\mathbf{u} \in V_2$, $\mathbf{u} \neq \mathbf{0}$, has an inverse $\mathbf{u}^{-1} \in V_2$ such that $\mathbf{u} \times \mathbf{u}^{-1} = \mathbf{u}^{-1} \times \mathbf{u} = \mathbf{i}$.

That is, the cross product is commutative and associative, $\mathbf{i}$ is the identity element relative to $\times$, and each nonzero vector has an inverse relative to $\times$. Incidentally,

$$\text{if } \mathbf{u} = a_1\mathbf{i} + a_2\mathbf{j}, \text{ then } \mathbf{u}^{-1} = \frac{1}{|\mathbf{u}|^2}(a_1\mathbf{i} - a_2\mathbf{j}).$$

We can summarize our remarks above by saying that V_2 is a *field* relative to the operations of addition and cross product, and that V_2 has a scalar multiplication satisfying 1.1(5)–(8) and also 4.3.

Although it was not known to Wessel and Argand, it is known to every college mathematics student today that the field V_2 is essentially (i.e., isomorphic to) the field C of complex numbers. The vector $\mathbf{j}$ has the property

$$\mathbf{j}^2 = \mathbf{j} \times \mathbf{j} = -\mathbf{i};$$

i.e., $\mathbf{j}$ is a square root of $-\mathbf{i}$. Thus associated with the vector

$$a\mathbf{i} + b\mathbf{j}$$

is the complex number

$$a + b\sqrt{-1}.$$

We do not denote $\sqrt{-1}$ by i, since i has another meaning in V_2.

Every complex number $z = a + b\sqrt{-1}$ has a trigonometric form

$$z = r(\cos\Theta + \sqrt{-1}\sin\Theta),$$

where $r = |z| = \sqrt{a^2 + b^2}$ and Θ is the angle shown in Fig. 4.2. If

$$z_k = r_k(\cos\Theta_k + \sqrt{-1}\sin\Theta_k), \qquad k = 1, 2,$$

then

$$z_1z_2 = r_1r_2[\cos(\Theta_1 + \Theta_2) + \sqrt{-1}\sin(\Theta_1 + \Theta_2)].$$

This shows that the product of complex numbers is the same as the cross product of vectors originally given by Wessel and Argand.

EXERCISES

1. Suppose we had defined the cross product in V_2 as follows: for all $a_i, b_i \in \mathsf{R}$,

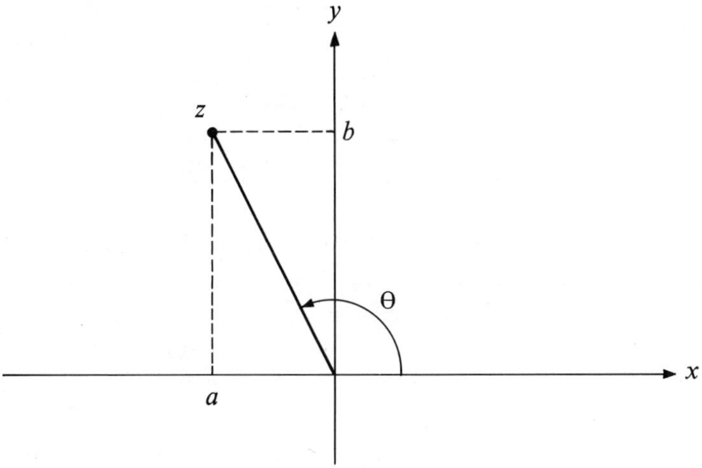

Figure 4.2

$$(a_1\mathbf{i} + a_2\mathbf{j}) \times (b_1\mathbf{i} + b_2\mathbf{j}) = (a_1b_1 + ra_2b_2)\mathbf{i} + (a_1b_2 + a_2b_1 + sa_2b_2)\mathbf{j},$$

where r and s are two fixed elements of **R**. Is V_2 a vector algebra? For what choices of r and s is V_2 a field?

2. THREE-DIMENSIONAL ALGEBRA

The vector algebra V_2 is not as useful as it might be in solving physical and geometrical problems for the simple reason that the physical world is three-dimensional rather than two-dimensional. Therefore, it is quite understandable that many mathematicians of the early nineteenth century tried to construct a physically and geometrically meaningful algebra from V_3. Ideally, they were looking for a way of defining a cross product in V_3 so that the resulting algebra was a field. In this endeavor they hoped to find a three-dimensional analogue of the complex number field. We know now what they did not know then, namely that no such three-dimensional field over **R** exists. Therefore the ideal solution was never attained.

Useful vector algebras were discovered in the nineteenth century, notably through the efforts of the Irish mathematician, physicist, and astronomer Hamilton and the German mathematician and philosopher Grassmann. These efforts were exploited by physicists such as Gibbs and Heaviside in the 1880s to give them a mathematical vehicle for theoretical physics.

We shall describe the algebra V_3 in the manner of the American mathematical physicist Gibbs. Assume that a right-handed rectangular coordinate sytem is chosen in E_3 and that $\mathbf{i}$, $\mathbf{j}$, and $\mathbf{k}$ are the usual unit vectors along the positive coordinate axes.

4.8. DEFINITION OF CROSS PRODUCT IN V_3. The cross product of vectors $\mathbf{u}$ and $\mathbf{v}$, written $\mathbf{u} \times \mathbf{v}$, is a vector whose length is obtained by multiplying the product of the lengths of $\mathbf{v}$ and $\mathbf{w}$ by the sine of the least angle Θ between them and whose direction is at right angles to $\mathbf{v}$ and $\mathbf{w}$ and on that side of the plane containing $\mathbf{v}$ and $\mathbf{w}$ on which the rotation of $\mathbf{v}$ to $\mathbf{w}$ through the angle Θ appears counterclockwise.

Since the sine of a right angle is 1, it follows from 4.8 that (Fig. 4.3)

4.9 $$\mathbf{i} \times \mathbf{j} = \mathbf{k}, \quad \mathbf{j} \times \mathbf{k} = \mathbf{i}, \quad \mathbf{k} \times \mathbf{i} = \mathbf{j}.$$

From the terminal point of $-\mathbf{k}$ the rotation from $\mathbf{j}$ to $\mathbf{i}$ appears counter-clockwise, and similarly for $-\mathbf{i}$ and $-\mathbf{j}$. That is (Fig. 4.4),

4.10 $$\mathbf{j} \times \mathbf{i} = -\mathbf{k}, \quad \mathbf{k} \times \mathbf{j} = -\mathbf{i}, \quad \mathbf{i} \times \mathbf{k} = -\mathbf{j}.$$

Finally, the sine of the angle 0 is 0, so that

4.11 $$\mathbf{i} \times \mathbf{i} = \mathbf{0}, \quad \mathbf{j} \times \mathbf{j} = \mathbf{0}, \quad \mathbf{k} \times \mathbf{k} = \mathbf{0}.$$

We shall not do so, but it may be shown that the cross product in V_3 has properties 4.2 and 4.3. Therefore V_3 is a vector algebra.

What we shall do is assume that the cross product of the vectors **i**, **j**, and **k** is given by 4.9–4.11. Then the cross product of any two vectors will be found by assuming that properties 4.2 and 4.3 hold. We illustrate how this is done below.

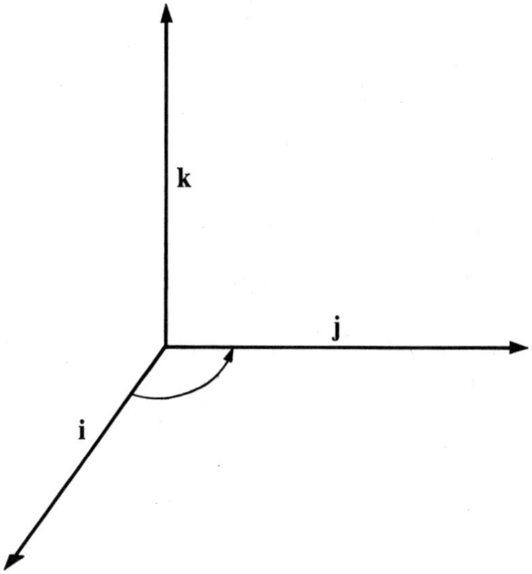

Figure 4.3

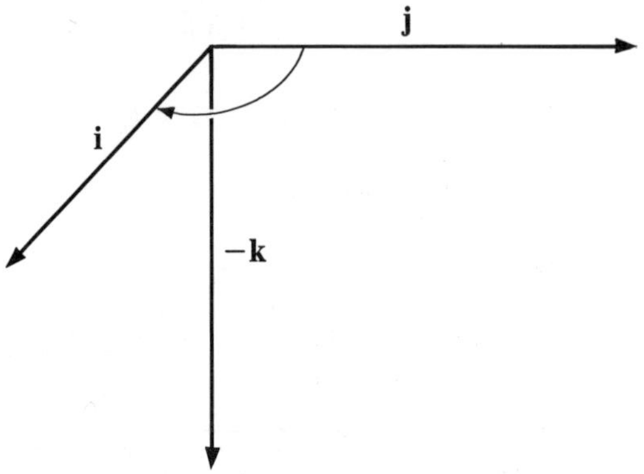

Figure 4.4

Example 1. Find $(3\mathbf{i} - \mathbf{j}) \times (2\mathbf{i} - 5\mathbf{k})$.

Solution: Using the distributive law (4.2), we have

$$\begin{aligned}(3\mathbf{i} - \mathbf{j}) \times (2\mathbf{i} - 5\mathbf{k}) &= (3\mathbf{i} - \mathbf{j}) \times (2\mathbf{i}) + (3\mathbf{i} - \mathbf{j}) \times (-5\mathbf{k}) \\ &= (3\mathbf{i}) \times (2\mathbf{i}) + (-\mathbf{j}) \times (2\mathbf{i}) + (3\mathbf{i}) \times (-5\mathbf{k}) \\ &\qquad + (-\mathbf{j}) \times (-5\mathbf{k}).\end{aligned}$$

Now using 4.3, we get

$$(3\mathbf{i} - \mathbf{j}) \times (2\mathbf{i} - 5\mathbf{k}) = 6(\mathbf{i} \times \mathbf{i}) - 2(\mathbf{j} \times \mathbf{i}) - 15(\mathbf{i} \times \mathbf{k}) + 5(\mathbf{j} \times \mathbf{k}).$$

Finally, using 4.9–4.11, we obtain

$$\begin{aligned}(3\mathbf{i} - \mathbf{j}) \times (2\mathbf{i} - 5\mathbf{k}) &= 6(\mathbf{0}) - 2(-\mathbf{k}) - 15(-\mathbf{j}) + 5(\mathbf{i}) \\ &= 5\mathbf{i} + 15\mathbf{j} + 2\mathbf{k}.\end{aligned}$$

Example 2. Find $(\mathbf{i} + \mathbf{j} - \mathbf{k}) \times (\mathbf{i} - \mathbf{j} + \mathbf{k})$.

Solution: Multiplying each term of $\mathbf{i} + \mathbf{j} - \mathbf{k}$ by each term of $\mathbf{i} - \mathbf{j} + \mathbf{k}$ (which is allowed by 4.2 and 4.3), we get

$$\begin{aligned}(\mathbf{i}+\mathbf{j}-\mathbf{k})\times(\mathbf{i}-\mathbf{j}+\mathbf{k}) &= \mathbf{i}\times\mathbf{i}-\mathbf{i}\times\mathbf{j}+\mathbf{i}\times\mathbf{k}+\mathbf{j}\times\mathbf{i}\\ &\quad -\mathbf{j}\times\mathbf{j}+\mathbf{j}\times\mathbf{k}-\mathbf{k}\times\mathbf{i}+\mathbf{k}\times\mathbf{j}\\ &\quad -\mathbf{k}\times\mathbf{k}\\ &= \mathbf{0}-\mathbf{k}-\mathbf{j}-\mathbf{k}-\mathbf{0}+\mathbf{i}-\mathbf{j}-\mathbf{i}-\mathbf{0}\\ &= -2\mathbf{j}-2\mathbf{k}.\end{aligned}$$

The general formula for finding the cross product of any two vectors may be found in the same way. It is as follows:

4.12 $$(a_1\mathbf{i}+a_2\mathbf{j}+a_3\mathbf{k})\times(b_1\mathbf{i}+b_2\mathbf{j}+b_3\mathbf{k}) = (a_2b_3-a_3b_2)\mathbf{i}+(a_3b_1-a_1b_3)\mathbf{j}+(a_1b_2-a_2b_1)\mathbf{k}.$$

We may, if we wish, take 4.12 to be the definition of cross product in V_3. Then properties 4.2, 4.3, 4.9, 4.10, and 4.11 may be shown to hold by straightforward, but tedious, computations.

Using determinants in a formal way, we may remember 4.12 as follows:

4.13 $$(a_1\mathbf{i}+a_2\mathbf{j}+a_3\mathbf{k})\times(b_1\mathbf{i}+b_2\mathbf{j}+b_3\mathbf{k}) = \begin{vmatrix}\mathbf{i} & \mathbf{j} & \mathbf{k}\\ a_1 & a_2 & a_3\\ b_1 & b_2 & b_3\end{vmatrix}.$$

We understand that the determinant is to be expanded by minors of the first row:

$$\begin{aligned}\begin{vmatrix}\mathbf{i} & \mathbf{j} & \mathbf{k}\\ a_1 & a_2 & a_3\\ b_1 & b_2 & b_3\end{vmatrix} &= \begin{vmatrix}a_2 & a_3\\ b_2 & b_3\end{vmatrix}\mathbf{i}-\begin{vmatrix}a_1 & a_3\\ b_1 & b_3\end{vmatrix}\mathbf{j}+\begin{vmatrix}a_1 & a_2\\ b_1 & b_2\end{vmatrix}\mathbf{k}\\ &= (a_2b_3-a_3b_2)\mathbf{i}-(a_1b_3-a_3b_1)\mathbf{j}+(a_1b_2-a_2b_1)\mathbf{k}.\end{aligned}$$

We see from 4.13 something that was evident from Gibbs's definition (4.8), namely that the cross product is *anticommutative:*

4.14 $$\mathbf{u}\times\mathbf{v} = -\mathbf{v}\times\mathbf{u} \text{ for all } \mathbf{u}, \mathbf{v}\in V_3.$$

Thus

$$\begin{vmatrix}\mathbf{i} & \mathbf{j} & \mathbf{k}\\ a_1 & a_2 & a_3\\ b_1 & b_2 & b_3\end{vmatrix} = -\begin{vmatrix}\mathbf{i} & \mathbf{j} & \mathbf{k}\\ b_1 & b_2 & b_3\\ a_1 & a_2 & a_3\end{vmatrix}.$$

This property is different from the commutative property which holds for multiplication in a field.

If we let $a_1 = a_2 = a_3 = 0$ in 4.12, we obtain the following property:

4.15 $$\mathbf{v} \times \mathbf{0} = \mathbf{0} \times \mathbf{v} = \mathbf{0} \text{ for all } \mathbf{v} \in V_3.$$

A simple example convinces us that the *cross product is not associative*. Thus $\mathbf{i} \times (\mathbf{j} \times \mathbf{j}) \neq (\mathbf{i} \times \mathbf{j}) \times \mathbf{j}$ because

$$\mathbf{i} \times (\mathbf{j} \times \mathbf{j}) = \mathbf{i} \times \mathbf{0} = \mathbf{0},$$
$$(\mathbf{i} \times \mathbf{j}) \times \mathbf{j} = \mathbf{k} \times \mathbf{j} = -\mathbf{i}.$$

Therefore the associative law of multiplication with which we are so accustomed to work may not be used in V_3. The actual difference between $\mathbf{u} \times (\mathbf{v} \times \mathbf{w})$ and $(\mathbf{u} \times \mathbf{v}) \times \mathbf{w}$ will be seen presently.

Since $\mathbf{v}$ and $\mathbf{w}$ are both perpendicular to $\mathbf{v} \times \mathbf{w}$ by 4.8, and since $\mathbf{u} \times (\mathbf{v} \times \mathbf{w})$ is also perpendicular to $\mathbf{v} \times \mathbf{w}$, evidently the vector $\mathbf{u} \times (\mathbf{v} \times \mathbf{w})$ is coplanar with $\mathbf{v}$ and $\mathbf{w}$. Therefore $\mathbf{u} \times (\mathbf{v} \times \mathbf{w})$ is a linear combination of $\mathbf{v}$ and $\mathbf{w}$. The actual relationship between them is as follows:

4.16 $$\mathbf{u} \times (\mathbf{v} \times \mathbf{w}) = (\mathbf{u} \cdot \mathbf{w})\mathbf{v} - (\mathbf{u} \cdot \mathbf{v})\mathbf{w}.$$

Proof: Let $\mathbf{u} = a_1\mathbf{i} + a_2\mathbf{j} + a_3\mathbf{k}$, $\mathbf{v} = b_1\mathbf{i} + b_2\mathbf{j} + b_3\mathbf{k}$, and $\mathbf{w} = c_1\mathbf{i} + c_2\mathbf{j} + c_3\mathbf{k}$. Then, by 4.12,

$$\begin{aligned}
\mathbf{u} \times (\mathbf{v} \times \mathbf{w}) &= [a_2(b_1c_2 - b_2c_1) - a_3(b_3c_1 - b_1c_3)]\mathbf{i} \\
&\quad + [a_3(b_2c_3 - b_3c_2) - a_1(b_1c_2 - b_2c_1)]\mathbf{j} \\
&\quad + [a_1(b_3c_1 - b_1c_3) - a_2(b_2c_3 - b_3c_2)]\mathbf{k} \\
&= [(\mathbf{u} \cdot \mathbf{w})b_1 - (\mathbf{u} \cdot \mathbf{v})c_1]\mathbf{i} + [(\mathbf{u} \cdot \mathbf{w})b_2 - (\mathbf{u} \cdot \mathbf{v})c_2]\mathbf{j} \\
&\quad + [(\mathbf{u} \cdot \mathbf{w})b_3 - (\mathbf{u} \cdot \mathbf{v})c_3]\mathbf{k} \\
&= (\mathbf{u} \cdot \mathbf{w})(b_1\mathbf{i} + b_2\mathbf{j} + b_3\mathbf{k}) - (\mathbf{u} \cdot \mathbf{v})(c_1\mathbf{i} + c_2\mathbf{j} + c_3\mathbf{k}) \\
&= (\mathbf{u} \cdot \mathbf{w})\mathbf{v} - (\mathbf{u} \cdot \mathbf{v})\mathbf{w}.
\end{aligned}$$

To find $(\mathbf{u} \times \mathbf{v}) \times \mathbf{w}$, we may use 4.14 and 4.16 as follows:

$$\begin{aligned}
(\mathbf{u} \times \mathbf{v}) \times \mathbf{w} &= -\mathbf{w} \times (\mathbf{u} \times \mathbf{v}) \\
&= -[(\mathbf{w} \cdot \mathbf{v})\mathbf{u} - (\mathbf{w} \cdot \mathbf{u})\mathbf{v}].
\end{aligned}$$

We may state this as follows:

4.17 $$(\mathbf{u} \times \mathbf{v}) \times \mathbf{w} = (\mathbf{u}\cdot\mathbf{w})\mathbf{v} - (\mathbf{v}\cdot\mathbf{w})\mathbf{u}.$$

Comparing 4.16 and 4.17, we see that

4.18 $\mathbf{u} \times (\mathbf{v} \times \mathbf{w}) = (\mathbf{u} \times \mathbf{v}) \times \mathbf{w}$ if and only if $(\mathbf{u}\cdot\mathbf{v})\mathbf{w} = (\mathbf{v}\cdot\mathbf{w})\mathbf{u}$.

For example, if $\mathbf{u}$, $\mathbf{v}$, and $\mathbf{w}$ are any three mutually perpendicular vectors, then $(\mathbf{u}\cdot\mathbf{v}) = (\mathbf{v}\cdot\mathbf{w}) = 0$ and $\mathbf{u} \times (\mathbf{v} \times \mathbf{w}) = (\mathbf{u} \times \mathbf{v}) \times \mathbf{w}$ by 4.18. In this case, however, it is clear from 4.16 and 4.17 that $\mathbf{u} \times (\mathbf{v} \times \mathbf{w}) = (\mathbf{u} \times \mathbf{v}) \times \mathbf{w} = \mathbf{0}$.

Example 3. Find $(\mathbf{i} + 2\mathbf{j}) \times [(\mathbf{j} - 3\mathbf{k}) \times (4\mathbf{i} - 7\mathbf{k})]$.

Solution: We have by 4.16 that

$$\begin{aligned}(\mathbf{i} + 2\mathbf{j}) \times [(\mathbf{j} - 3\mathbf{k}) \times (4\mathbf{i} - 7\mathbf{k})] &= [(\mathbf{i} + 2\mathbf{j})\cdot(4\mathbf{i} - 7\mathbf{k})](\mathbf{j} - 3\mathbf{k}) \\ &\quad - [(\mathbf{i} + 2\mathbf{j})\cdot(\mathbf{j} - 3\mathbf{k})](4\mathbf{i} - 7\mathbf{k}) \\ &= 4(\mathbf{j} - 3\mathbf{k}) - 2(4\mathbf{i} - 7\mathbf{k}) \\ &= -8\mathbf{i} + 4\mathbf{j} + 2\mathbf{k}.\end{aligned}$$

The triple cross product is given in terms of the dot product in both 4.16 and 4.17. Another relationship between the dot and cross products is given below.

If $\mathbf{u} = a_1\mathbf{i} + a_2\mathbf{j} + a_3\mathbf{k}$, $\mathbf{v} = b_1\mathbf{i} + b_2\mathbf{j} + b_3\mathbf{k}$, and $\mathbf{w} = c_1\mathbf{i} + c_2\mathbf{j} + c_3\mathbf{k}$, then

$$\begin{aligned}(\mathbf{u} \times \mathbf{v})\cdot\mathbf{w} &= (a_2b_3 - a_3b_2)c_1 + (a_3b_1 - a_1b_3)c_2 + (a_1b_2 - a_2b_1)c_3 \\ &= a_1(b_2c_3 - b_3c_2) + a_2(b_3c_1 - b_1c_3) + a_3(b_1c_2 - b_2c_1) \\ &= \mathbf{u}\cdot(\mathbf{v} \times \mathbf{w}).\end{aligned}$$

That is,

4.19 $$(\mathbf{u} \times \mathbf{v})\cdot\mathbf{w} = \mathbf{u}\cdot(\mathbf{v} \times \mathbf{w}).$$

We may use 4.16 and 4.19 to compute the length of vector $\mathbf{u} \times \mathbf{v}$. Thus

$$\begin{aligned}(\mathbf{u} \times \mathbf{v})\cdot(\mathbf{u} \times \mathbf{v}) &= \mathbf{u}\cdot[\mathbf{v} \times (\mathbf{u} \times \mathbf{v})] \\ &= \mathbf{u}\cdot[(\mathbf{v}\cdot\mathbf{v})\mathbf{u} - (\mathbf{v}\cdot\mathbf{u})\mathbf{v}] \\ &= (\mathbf{v}\cdot\mathbf{v})(\mathbf{u}\cdot\mathbf{u}) - (\mathbf{v}\cdot\mathbf{u})(\mathbf{u}\cdot\mathbf{v}),\end{aligned}$$

and we have

4.20 $$|\mathbf{u} \times \mathbf{v}| = \sqrt{|\mathbf{u}|^2|\mathbf{v}|^2 - (\mathbf{u}\cdot\mathbf{v})^2}.$$

If we recall that, by 3.1, $\mathbf{u}\cdot\mathbf{v} = |\mathbf{u}|\,|\mathbf{v}| \cos \Theta$, where Θ is the angle between vectors $\mathbf{u}$ and $\mathbf{v}$, then we have

$$\begin{aligned} |\mathbf{u}|^2|\mathbf{v}|^2 - (\mathbf{u}\cdot\mathbf{v})^2 &= |\mathbf{u}|^2|\mathbf{v}|^2 - |\mathbf{u}|^2|\mathbf{v}|^2 \cos^2 \Theta \\ &= |\mathbf{u}|^2|\mathbf{v}|^2(1 - \cos^2 \Theta) \\ &= |\mathbf{u}|^2|\mathbf{v}|^2 \sin^2 \Theta. \end{aligned}$$

Since $\sin \Theta \geq 0$ if $0 \leq \Theta \leq \pi$, we may put 4.20 in the form:

4.21 $$|\mathbf{u} \times \mathbf{v}| = |\mathbf{u}|\,|\mathbf{v}| \sin \Theta.$$

Checking back to 4.8, we see that this is the length of $\mathbf{u} \times \mathbf{v}$ as given by Gibbs.

In geometrical language, $|\mathbf{u} \times \mathbf{v}|$ is the area of the parallelogram having vectors $\mathbf{u}$ and $\mathbf{v}$ as adjacent sides (Fig. 4.5). This is clear from 4.21, since $|\mathbf{u}| \sin \Theta$ is the distance between $\mathbf{v}$ and its opposite side in the parallelogram. Hence the area is $|\mathbf{v}|(|\mathbf{u}| \sin \Theta)$. The parallelogram of Fig. 4.5 has area 0 if and only if $\Theta = 0$ or $\Theta = \pi$, i.e., if and only if $\mathbf{u}$ and $\mathbf{v}$ are collinear and hence scalar multiples of each other. We state this result as follows.

4.22. THEOREM. If $\mathbf{u}, \mathbf{v} \in V_3$, $\mathbf{u} \neq \mathbf{0}$, then

$$\mathbf{u} \times \mathbf{v} = \mathbf{0} \text{ if and only if } \mathbf{v} = a\mathbf{u} \text{ for some } a \in \mathsf{R}.$$

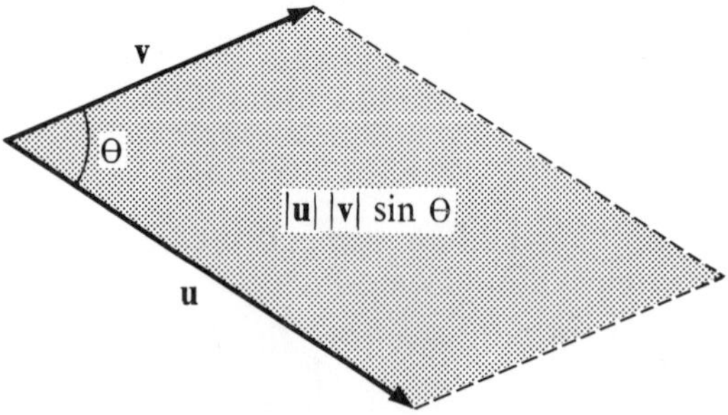

Figure 4.5

As a special case of 4.22, we have $\mathbf{u} \times \mathbf{u} = \mathbf{0}$ for all $\mathbf{u} \in V_3$. Thus we also have

$$\mathbf{u} \cdot (\mathbf{u} \times \mathbf{v}) = (\mathbf{u} \times \mathbf{u}) \cdot \mathbf{v} = 0 \text{ for all } \mathbf{u}, \mathbf{v} \in V_3.$$

That is, $\mathbf{u}$ is perepndicular to $\mathbf{u} \times \mathbf{v}$ and, similarly, $\mathbf{v}$ is perpendicular to $\mathbf{u} \times \mathbf{v}$, as stated in the definition of cross product given by Gibbs (4.8).

We mention in passing that there is no identity element in V_3 relative to the cross product operation. That is, there is no $\mathbf{u} \in V_3$ such that

$$\mathbf{u} \times \mathbf{v} = \mathbf{v} \times \mathbf{u} = \mathbf{v} \text{ for all } \mathbf{v} \in V_3.$$

For $\mathbf{u} \times \mathbf{v}$ is perpendicular to $\mathbf{v}$, and hence cannot equal $\mathbf{v}$ unless $\mathbf{v} = \mathbf{0}$.

EXERCISES

Given that $\mathbf{v} = 2\mathbf{i} - \mathbf{j} + 3\mathbf{k}$, $\mathbf{w} = -4\mathbf{i} + \mathbf{j} + 5\mathbf{k}$, and $\mathbf{y} = 7\mathbf{i} + 2\mathbf{j} - 2\mathbf{k}$, find each of Exercises 1–12.

1. $\mathbf{v} \times \mathbf{w}$.
2. $\mathbf{v} \cdot (\mathbf{w} \times \mathbf{y})$.
3. $\mathbf{v} \times (\mathbf{w} \times \mathbf{y})$.
4. $(\mathbf{v} \times \mathbf{w}) \times \mathbf{y}$.
5. $\mathbf{v} \times (\mathbf{w} + \mathbf{y})$.
6. $(\mathbf{v} \times \mathbf{w}) \cdot \mathbf{y}$.
7. $(\mathbf{v} - \mathbf{w}) \times \mathbf{y}$.
8. $(2\mathbf{v} + 3\mathbf{w}) \cdot \mathbf{y}$.
9. $(3\mathbf{w}) \times (3\mathbf{v} - 2\mathbf{y})$.
10. $\mathbf{v} \times (\mathbf{w} \times \mathbf{v})$.
11. $(\mathbf{w} \times 2\mathbf{w}) \times \mathbf{y}$.
12. $(\mathbf{v} \times \mathbf{w}) \times (\mathbf{w} \times \mathbf{y})$.
13. Show that $(\mathbf{u} + \mathbf{v}) \times (\mathbf{u} - \mathbf{v}) = 2(\mathbf{u} \times \mathbf{v})$ for all $\mathbf{u}, \mathbf{v} \in V_3$.
14. Let $\mathbf{u}$ be a unit vector along a line L and let $\mathbf{v}$ be any vector in V_3. Prove that the projection $\mathbf{v}'$ of $\mathbf{v}$ on L (see Fig. 4.6) is given by $\mathbf{v}' = (\mathbf{u} \cdot \mathbf{v})\mathbf{u}$.

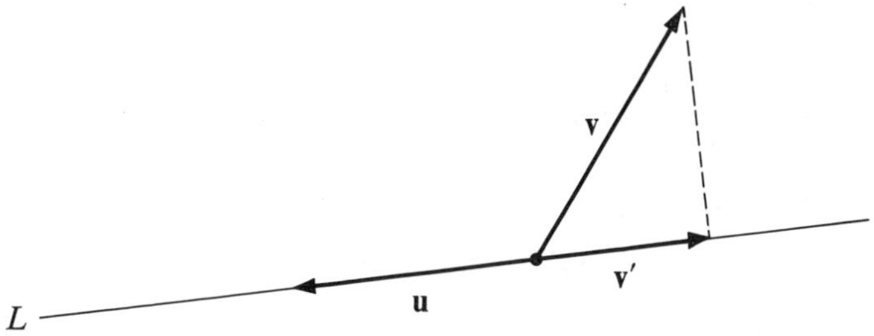

Figure 4.6

15. If $\mathbf{u}$, $\mathbf{v}$, and $\mathbf{w}$ are the three sides of a triangle, then prove that $\mathbf{u} \times \mathbf{v} = \mathbf{v} \times \mathbf{w} = \mathbf{w} \times \mathbf{u}$.

16. Prove the Jacobi identity:
$(\mathbf{u} \times \mathbf{v}) \times \mathbf{w} + (\mathbf{v} \times \mathbf{w}) \times \mathbf{u} + (\mathbf{w} \times \mathbf{u}) \times \mathbf{v} = \mathbf{0}$ for all $\mathbf{u}, \mathbf{v}, \mathbf{w} \in V_3$.

17. Prove the Lagrange identity:
$(\mathbf{u} \times \mathbf{v}) \cdot (\mathbf{w} \times \mathbf{y}) = (\mathbf{u} \cdot \mathbf{w})(\mathbf{v} \cdot \mathbf{y}) - (\mathbf{u} \cdot \mathbf{y})(\mathbf{v} \cdot \mathbf{w})$ for all $\mathbf{u}, \mathbf{v}, \mathbf{w}, \mathbf{y} \in V_3$.

18. If $\mathbf{u} = a_1\mathbf{i} + a_2\mathbf{j} + a_3\mathbf{k}$, $\mathbf{v} = b_1\mathbf{i} + b_2\mathbf{j} + b_3\mathbf{k}$, and $\mathbf{w} = c_1\mathbf{i} + c_2\mathbf{j} + c_3\mathbf{k}$, then prove that

$$\mathbf{u} \cdot (\mathbf{v} \times \mathbf{w}) = \begin{vmatrix} a_1 & a_2 & a_3 \\ b_1 & b_2 & b_3 \\ c_1 & c_2 & c_3 \end{vmatrix}.$$

19. Express $(\mathbf{u} \times \mathbf{v}) \times (\mathbf{y} \times \mathbf{z})$ as a linear combination of the vectors $\mathbf{u}$, $\mathbf{v}$, $\mathbf{y}$, and $\mathbf{z}$.

20. Prove that $|\mathbf{u} + \mathbf{v}|^2 = |\mathbf{u}|^2 + |\mathbf{v}|^2$ if and only if $\mathbf{u} \cdot \mathbf{v} = 0$.

3. LINES IN SPACE

Given a rectangular coordinate system in E_3, every line and plane in E_3 may be described by linear equations. Consider first of all a line L passing through a point P with coordinates (a_1, a_2, a_3) and having the direction of a nonzero vector

$$\mathbf{v} = h_1\mathbf{i} + h_2\mathbf{j} + h_3\mathbf{k}.$$

Then a point $\mathbf{Q}$ is on line L if and only if (Fig. 4.7)

$$\mathbf{PQ} = t\mathbf{v} \text{ for some } t \in \mathsf{R}.$$

In other words,

$$L = \{Q \in E_3 \mid \mathbf{PQ} = t\mathbf{v} \text{ for some } t \in \mathsf{R}\}$$

if we consider L as a set of points in E_3. If Q has coordinates (x, y, z), then

$$\mathbf{PQ} = (x - a_1)\mathbf{i} + (y - a_2)\mathbf{j} + (z - a_3)\mathbf{k},$$
$$t\mathbf{v} = (th_1)\mathbf{i} + (th_2)\mathbf{j} + (th_3)\mathbf{k},$$

and Q is on L if and only if

$$x - a_1 = th_1, \quad y - a_2 = th_2, \quad z - a_3 = th_3 \text{ for some } t \in \mathsf{R}.$$

That is, L is the *graph* of the following set of equations:

4.23 $$x = a_1 + h_1t, \quad y = a_2 + h_2t, \quad z = a_3 + h_3t.$$

This means that L consists of all points with coordinates (x, y, z) satisfying 4.23 for some $t \in \mathbf{R}$. Equations 4.23 give x, y, and z in terms of a variable t, called a *parameter*. For this reason equations 4.23 are called *parametric equations* of line L.

Example 1. Find parametric equations of the line L passing through the point P with coordinate $(-1, 3, 5)$ and in the direction of $\mathbf{v} = 2\mathbf{i} - \mathbf{j}$.

Solution: Letting $(a_1, a_2, a_3) = (-1, 3, 5)$ and $h_1\mathbf{i} + h_2\mathbf{j} + h_3\mathbf{k} = 2\mathbf{i} - \mathbf{j}$ in 4.23, we get

$$x = -1 + 2t, \quad y = 3 - t, \quad z = 5$$

as parametric equations of L. If, for example, we let $t = 7$, we get $(13, -4, 5)$ as (the coordinates of) a point on L. We might ask where L crosses the coordinate planes. By letting $x = 0$, we see that $-1 + 2t = 0$ and $t = \frac{1}{2}$. Then letting $t = \frac{1}{2}$, we get the point $(0, \frac{5}{2}, 5)$ on L, which is the point where L crosses the yz-plane. Similarly, $y = 0$ if $t = 3$, and $(5, 0, 5)$ is the point at which L crosses the xz-plane. The line L does not cross the xy-plane, since $z = 5 \neq 0$ for all values of t. In other words, L is parallel to the xy-plane.

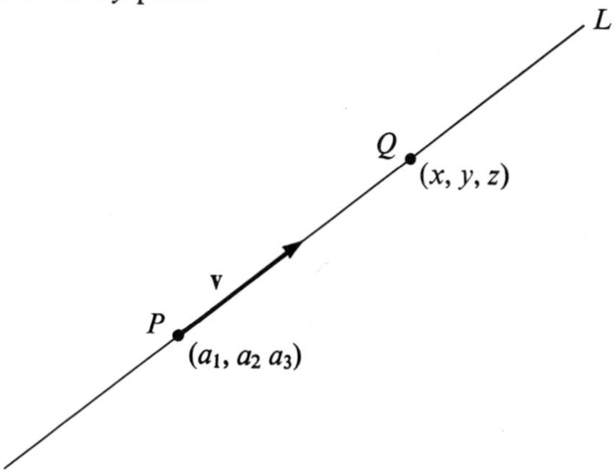

Figure 4.7

We can get another form of an equation for L by using 4.22. As above, let (a_1, a_2, a_3) be the coordinates of a point P on L and $\mathbf{v} = h_1\mathbf{i} + h_2\mathbf{j} + h_3\mathbf{k}$ be the direction of L. Then a point $Q \in E_3$ is on L if and only if

$$\mathbf{v} \times \mathbf{PQ} = \mathbf{0}.$$

Letting Q have coordinates (x, y, z), we have $\mathbf{PQ} = (x - a_1)\mathbf{i} + (y - a_2)\mathbf{j} + (z - a_3)\mathbf{k}$ and the equation above has the form

4.24 $$(h_1\mathbf{i} + h_2\mathbf{j} + h_3\mathbf{k}) \times [(x - a_1)\mathbf{i} + (y - a_2)\mathbf{j} + (z - a_3)\mathbf{k}] = \mathbf{0}.$$

Expanding 4.24, we get

$$[h_2(z - a_3) - h_3(y - a_2)]\mathbf{i} + [h_3(x - a_1) - h_1(z - a_3)]\mathbf{j} + [h_1(y - a_2) - h_2(x - a_1)]\mathbf{k} = \mathbf{0}.$$

Since the vectors **i**, **j**, and **k** are linearly independent, the coefficients of **i**, **j**, and **k** in this equation are zero by 2.3. Thus

$$h_2(z - a_3) - h_3(y - a_2) = 0, \quad h_3(x - a_1) - h_1(z - a_3) = 0, \quad h_1(y - a_2) - h_2(x - a_1) = 0$$

or

4.25 $$\begin{cases} h_2(x - a_1) = h_1(y - a_2) \\ h_3(x - a_1) = h_1(z - a_3) \\ h_3(y - a_2) = h_2(z - a_3) \end{cases}$$

is a system of equations of L. That is, a point with coordinates (x, y, z) is on L if and only if x, y, and z are solutions of 4.25. We call 4.25 the *symmetric form* of the equation of a line.

Example 2. Let line L pass through the point with coordinates $(3, -3, 4)$ and in the direction $\mathbf{v} = \mathbf{i} + 3\mathbf{j} - 2\mathbf{k}$. Find the symmetric form of the equation of L.

Solution: Letting $(a_1, a_2, a_3) = (3, -3, 4)$ and $h_1\mathbf{i} + h_2\mathbf{j} + h_3\mathbf{k} = \mathbf{i} + 3\mathbf{j} - 2\mathbf{k}$, we find that system 4.25 becomes

(1) $$\begin{cases} 3(x - 3) = (y + 3) \\ -2(x - 3) = (z - 4) \\ -2(y + 3) = 3(z - 4). \end{cases}$$

To find the point where L crosses the xy-plane, we let $z = 0$ in (1). Then we get

$$-2(x - 3) = -4, \text{ or } x = 5,$$

$$-2(y + 3) = 3(-4), \text{ or } y = 3.$$

Hence $(5, 3, 0)$ is the point at which L crosses the xy-plane. Letting $y = 0$ in (1), we get $x = 4$ and $z = 2$. Therefore $(4, 0, 2)$ is the point at which L crosses the xz-plane. Similarly, letting $x = 0$ in (1), we find that $(0, -12, 10)$ is the point at which L crosses the yz-plane. We can find other points on L by giving other values to x, y, or z. For example, if $x = -2$, then by (1)

$$3(-2 - 3) = y + 3, \text{ or } y = -18,$$

$$-2(-2 - 3) = z - 4, \text{ or } z = 14.$$

Hence $(-2, -18, 14)$ is on L.

Let L be the line passing through the point P with coordinates (a_1, a_2, a_3) and in the direction of a vector $\mathbf{v}$. We can consider L to be a *directed line*, with the direction of L being that of $\mathbf{v}$. Then the ray

$$L^+ = \{Q \in E_3 \mid \mathbf{PQ} = t\mathbf{v} \text{ for all } t \geq 0\}$$

is called the *positive ray* on L with endpoint P, and

$$L^- = \{Q \in E_3 \mid \mathbf{PQ} = t\mathbf{v} \text{ for all } t \leq 0\}$$

is called the *negative ray* on L with endpoint P.

Example 3. Describe the positive and negative rays with endpoint P of the line L passing through the points P and Q with respective coordinates $(2, 2, 2)$ and $(3, 2, 4)$, if the direction of L is from P toward Q.

Solution: The vector $\mathbf{PQ}$ with components $(3 - 2, 2 - 2, 4 - 2)$ may be taken to be a direction $\mathbf{v}$ of L:

$$\mathbf{v} = \mathbf{PQ} = \mathbf{i} + 2\mathbf{k}.$$

Line L is sketched in Fig. 4.8, and its positive ray L^+ and negative ray L^- having P as endpoint are indicated. Parametric equations of L are as follows:

$$x = 2 + t, \quad y = 2, \quad z = 2 + 2t.$$

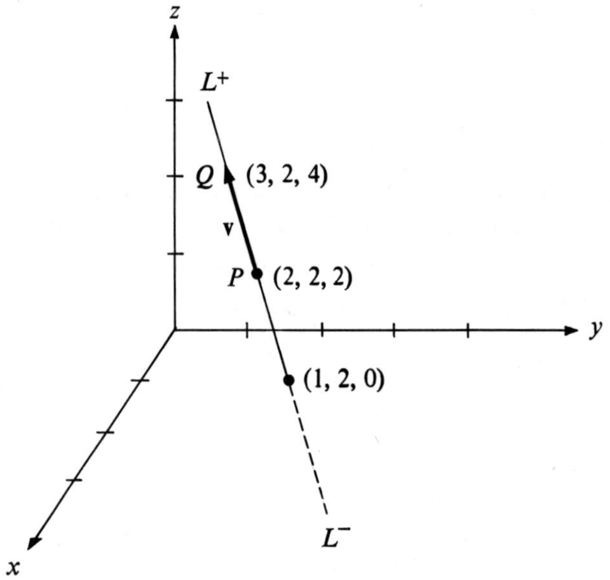

Figure 4.8

Thus

$$L^{+} = \{(2 + t, 2, 2 + 2t) \mid t \geq 0\},$$
$$L^{-} = \{(2 + t, 2, 2 + 2t) \mid t \leq 0\}.$$

For example, if we let $t = 1$, then we obtain the point $Q = (3, 2, 4)$ on the positive ray; and if we let $t = -1$, then we obtain the point $(1, 2, 0)$ on the negative ray.

If we let the direction of line L be a unit vector $\mathbf{u}$, then the parameter t measures distances along L. That is, if P is a given point on L and

$$L = \{Q \in E_3 \mid \mathbf{PQ} = t\mathbf{u} \text{ for some } t \in \mathsf{R}\},$$

then t is the directed distance from P to Q on the line L if $\mathbf{PQ} = t\mathbf{u}$. This is true because

$$|\mathbf{PQ}| = |t\mathbf{u}| = |t|\,|\mathbf{u}| = |t|.$$

If $t > 0$, then Q is on the positive ray, whereas if $t < 0$, then t is on the negative ray.

For example, vector $\mathbf{v}$ in Example 3 has length $\sqrt{5}$. Therefore

$$\mathbf{u} = \frac{1}{\sqrt{5}}\mathbf{v} = \frac{1}{\sqrt{5}}(\mathbf{i} + 2\mathbf{k})$$

is a unit vector having the same direction as $\mathbf{v}$. The point Q on the positive ray two units from P is given by

$$\mathbf{PQ} = 2\mathbf{u} = \frac{2\sqrt{5}}{5}(\mathbf{i} + 2\mathbf{k}).$$

If (x, y, z) are the coordinates of Q, then

$$(x - 2)\mathbf{i} + (y - 2)\mathbf{j} + (z - 2)\mathbf{k} = \frac{2\sqrt{5}}{5}(\mathbf{i} + 2\mathbf{k})$$

and

$$x - 2 = \frac{2\sqrt{5}}{5}, \quad y - 2 = 0, \quad z - 2 = \frac{4\sqrt{5}}{5}.$$

Thus Q has coordinates

$$\left(2 + \frac{2\sqrt{5}}{5}, 2, 2 + \frac{4\sqrt{5}}{5}\right).$$

As special examples, we have the coordinate axes in the directions **i**, **j**, and **k**. Thus each axis has the origin O as a point on it. The x-axis is given by

$$\{Q \in E_3 \mid \mathbf{OQ} = t\mathbf{i} \text{ for some } t \in \mathsf{R}\}$$

and has parametric equations

$$x = t, \quad y = 0, \quad z = 0.$$

The positive ray of the x-axis is $\{Q \in E_3 \mid \mathbf{OQ} = t\mathbf{i}, t \geq 0\}$, which we normally call the positive x-axis. The y- and z-axes are given similarly.

If line L has unit direction vector **u**, the angles between **u** and **i**, **u** and **j**, and **u** and **k** are called the *direction angles* of L. They are the angles α, β, and γ of Fig. 4.9. The cosines of α, β, and γ are called the *direction cosines* of L. Since **u**, **i**, **j**, and **k** are unit vectors, evidently

$$\cos\alpha = \mathbf{u}\cdot\mathbf{i}, \quad \cos\beta = \mathbf{u}\cdot\mathbf{j}, \quad \cos\gamma = \mathbf{u}\cdot\mathbf{k}.$$

In other words, if $\mathbf{u} = h_1\mathbf{i} + h_2\mathbf{j} + h_3\mathbf{k}$, then $\mathbf{u}\cdot\mathbf{i} = h_1$, and so on, and

$$h_1 = \cos\alpha, \quad h_2 = \cos\beta, \quad h_3 = \cos\gamma.$$

Since $h_1^2 + h_2^2 + h_3^2 = |\mathbf{u}|^2 = 1$, we have

4.26
$$\cos^2\alpha + \cos^2\beta + \cos^2\gamma = 1.$$

Example 4. If line L has direction $\mathbf{v} = 2\mathbf{i} + 4\mathbf{j} - 4\mathbf{k}$, find the direction cosines of L.

Solution: We first find the unit vector **u** in the direction of L. Since $|\mathbf{v}|^2 = 2^2 + 4^2 + (-4)^2 = 36$, $|\mathbf{v}| = 6$ and

$$\mathbf{u} = \tfrac{1}{6}\mathbf{v} = \tfrac{1}{3}\mathbf{i} + \tfrac{2}{3}\mathbf{j} - \tfrac{2}{3}\mathbf{k}.$$

Hence

$$\cos\alpha = \mathbf{u}\cdot\mathbf{i} = \tfrac{1}{3}, \quad \cos\beta = \mathbf{u}\cdot\mathbf{j} = \tfrac{2}{3}, \quad \cos\gamma = \mathbf{u}\cdot\mathbf{k} = -\tfrac{2}{3}.$$

From a table of trigonometric functions, we find

$$\alpha = 70°32', \quad \beta = 48°11', \quad \gamma = 131°49', \text{ approx.}$$

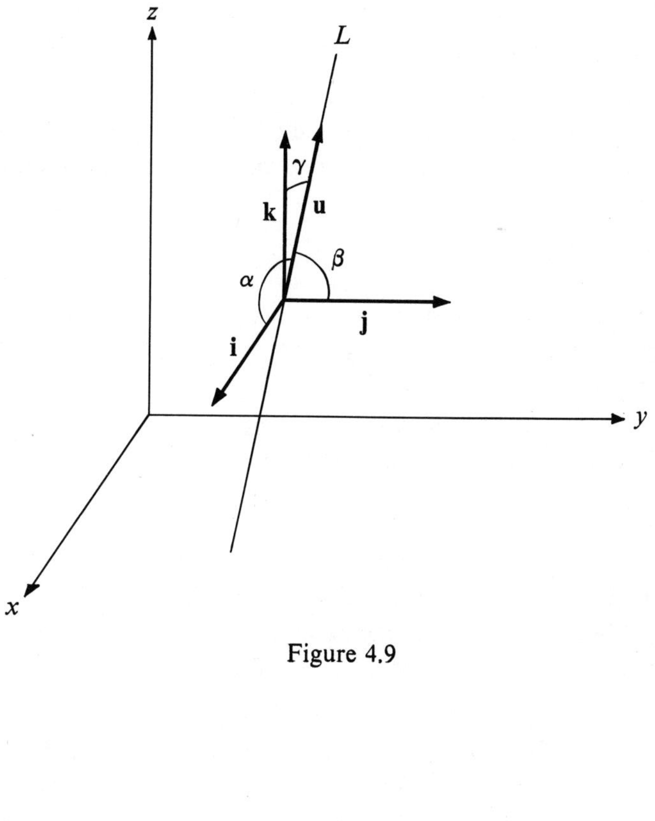

Figure 4.9

EXERCISES

In each of Exercises 1–6 find parametric equations of the given line. Also find the points where the line crosses the coordinate planes.

1. Line on point (1, 5, 3) with direction $\mathbf{i} + 2\mathbf{j} - 7\mathbf{k}$.
2. Line on point (0, −4, 9) with direction $3\mathbf{i} - 7\mathbf{k}$.
3. Line on point (−3, 3, 4) with direction $3\mathbf{i} - 2\mathbf{j} + 3\mathbf{k}$.
4. Line on point (2, −4, 8) with direction $\mathbf{j} + \mathbf{k}$.
5. Line on point (1, 1, 1) with direction $\mathbf{i} + \mathbf{j} + \mathbf{k}$.
6. Line on point (−1, 1, −1) with direction $-2\mathbf{i} + \mathbf{j} + 3\mathbf{k}$.

In each of Exercises 7–12 find the symmetric form of the equation of the line passing through points P and Q, taking the line to have direction from P toward Q. Also find the points where the line crosses the coordinate planes.

7. $P = (4, 7, -3)$, $Q = (5, 2, 2)$.
8. $P = (0, 0, 0)$, $Q = (3, -1, 4)$.
9. $P = (1, 2, 3)$, $Q = (3, 2, 1)$.
10. $P = (11, 4, -13)$, $Q = (7, 3, -15)$.
11. $P = (-2, 3, 5)$, $Q = (4, 1, -1)$.
12. $P = (0, 3, 2)$, $Q = (0, 2, 2)$.
13. Find the direction cosines of the line with direction:
    a. $4\mathbf{i} - 4\mathbf{j} - 2\mathbf{k}$. b. $\mathbf{i} - \mathbf{j} + \mathbf{k}$.
    c. $\mathbf{i} - \mathbf{k}$. d. $3\mathbf{i} + 4\mathbf{j}$.
14. If $\pi/3$ and $3\pi/4$ are two of the direction angles of a line, then find all possible values of the third direction angle.
15. Prove that only one of the direction angles of a line can be less than $\pi/4$.

4. PLANES IN SPACE

Through a given point P in space there is a unique plane p perpendicular to a given nonzero vector $\mathbf{v}$ (Fig. 4.10). If we consider p as a set of points in E_3, then

$$p = \{Q \in E_3 \mid \mathbf{PQ} \cdot \mathbf{v} = 0\}.$$

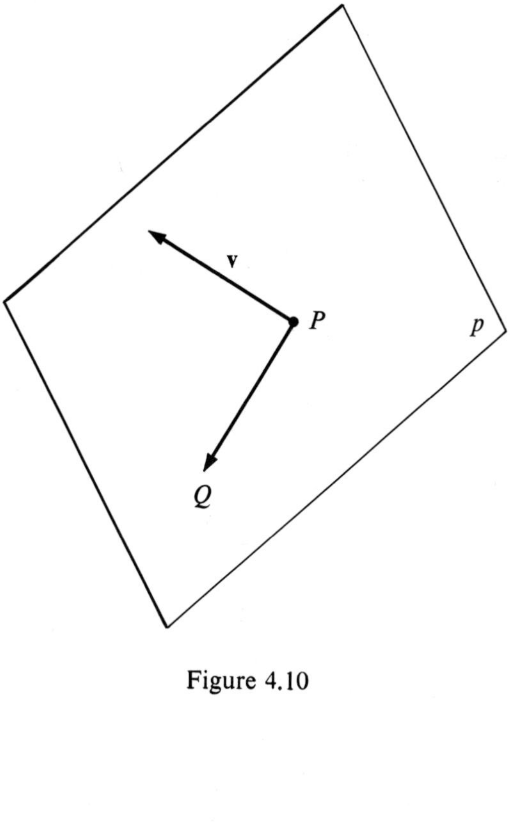

Figure 4.10

By giving coordinates to the points P and Q and components to $\mathbf{v}$, we can obtain an equation for the plane $\mathbf{v}$. Thus let P and Q have respective coordinates (a_1, a_2, a_3) and (x, y, z), and let $\mathbf{v} = h_1\mathbf{i} + h_2\mathbf{j} + h_3\mathbf{k}$. Then

$$\mathbf{PQ} = (x - a_1)\mathbf{i} + (y - a_2)\mathbf{j} + (z - a_3)\mathbf{k}$$

and

$$\mathbf{PQ} \cdot \mathbf{v} = (x - a_1)h_1 + (y - a_2)h_2 + (z - a_3)h_3.$$

Hence plane p is the graph of the equation

4.27 $$h_1(x - a_1) + h_2(y - a_2) + h_3(z - a_3) = 0$$

in the sense that the point Q with coordinates (x, y, z) is on p if and only if x, y, and z satisfy equation 4.27.

A nonzero vector perpendicular to a plane is often called a *normal vector* of the plane. Equation 4.27 of a plane contains the coordinates (a_1, a_2, a_3) of a point on the plane and the components (h_1, h_2, h_3) of a normal vector of the plane.

Example 1. Find an equation of the plane passing through the point $(-1, 3, 1)$ and having normal vector $2\mathbf{i} - \mathbf{j} + 7\mathbf{k}$.

Solution: By 4.27,

$$2(x + 1) - (y - 3) + 7(z - 1) = 0$$

or

$$2x - y + 7z = 2$$

is an equation of the plane. We can find where the plane crosses the coordinate axes by giving two of the variables x, y, z the value 0 and solving the resulting equation for the third variable. Thus if $y = 0$ and $z = 0$, then $2x = 2$ and $x = 1$. Hence the plane crosses the x-axis at the point $(1, 0, 0)$ and we call 1 the *x-intercept* of the plane. By letting $x = 0$ and $z = 0$, we get $y = -2$. Thus -2 is the *y-intercept;* i.e., the plane crosses the y-axis at the point $(0, -2, 0)$. Finally, by letting $x = 0$ and $y = 0$ in the equation, we find that $\frac{2}{7}$ is the *z-intercept* and hence that the plane crosses the z-axis at the point $(0, 0, \frac{2}{7})$.

Any three noncollinear points in E_3 are contained in a unique plane, which may easily be found as follows.

Example 2. Find an equation of the plane passing through the three points A, B, and C with respective coordinates (1, 2, 1), (2, 3, 4), and (0, 4, 5).

Solution: Vectors **AB** and **AC** have respective components $(2 - 1, 3 - 2, 4 - 1)$ and $(0 - 1, 4 - 2, 5 - 1)$. Thus

$$\mathbf{AB} = \mathbf{i} + \mathbf{j} + 3\mathbf{k}, \quad \mathbf{AC} = -\mathbf{i} + 2\mathbf{j} + 4\mathbf{k}.$$

An obvious normal vector of the plane is $\mathbf{v} = \mathbf{AB} \times \mathbf{AC}$, computed as follows:

$$\begin{aligned} \mathbf{v} &= (\mathbf{i} + \mathbf{j} + 3\mathbf{k}) \times (-\mathbf{i} + 2\mathbf{j} + 4\mathbf{k}) \\ &= (4 - 6)\mathbf{i} + (-3 - 4)\mathbf{j} + (2 + 1)\mathbf{k} \\ &= -2\mathbf{i} - 7\mathbf{j} + 3\mathbf{k}. \end{aligned}$$

Incidentally, the fact that $\mathbf{v} \neq \mathbf{0}$ shows that A, B, and C are noncollinear. Using point A in equation 4.27, we obtain

$$-2(x - 1) - 7(y - 2) + 3(z - 1) = 0$$

or

$$2x + 7y - 3z = 13$$

as an equation of the plane passing through A, B, and C. The intercepts of the plane are easily seen to be $\frac{13}{2}$, $\frac{13}{7}$, and $-\frac{13}{3}$.

We saw above that every plane in E_3 has a linear equation of the form 4.27. It is true, conversely, that every linear equation of the form

4.28 $$ax + by + cz = d,$$

where $a, b, c, d \in \mathsf{R}$ and not all of a, b, and c are zero, has a plane in E_3 as its graph. To see this, let (x_1, y_1, z_1) be any solution of 4.28 and let $\mathbf{v} = a\mathbf{i} + b\mathbf{j} + c\mathbf{k}$. Then the plane p passing through the point with coordinates (x_1, y_1, z_1) and having normal vector $\mathbf{v}$ has equation

$$a(x - x_1) + b(y - y_1) + c(z - z_1) = 0$$

or

$$ax + by + cz = ax_1 + by_1 + cz_1.$$

However, $ax_1 + by_1 + cz_1 = d$ since (x_1, y_1, z_1) is a solution of 4.28. Hence the graph of 4.28 is plane p.

Example 3. Describe the graph in E_3 of the equation

$$2x + y + 3z = 6.$$

Solution: We easily check that $(3, 0, 0)$ is a solution of this equation. Therefore the graph of this equation is the plane passing through the point $(3, 0, 0)$ and having normal vector $2\mathbf{i} + \mathbf{j} + 3\mathbf{k}$. We could equally well describe the graph by finding three noncollinear points on the graph, such as $(3, 0, 0)$, $(0, 6, 0)$, and $(0, 0, 2)$, and then stating that the graph is the plane through these three points.

Two planes are parallel if and only if their normal vectors are parallel, i.e., are dependent. Thus the coefficients of x, y, and z in the equations of parallel planes are proportional. For example,

$$2x - y + 3z = 7 \quad \text{and} \quad 6x - 3y + 9z = -4$$

are equations of parallel planes.

Similarly, two planes are perpendicular if and only if their normal vectors are perpendicular. Therefore if $\mathbf{v}$ and $\mathbf{w}$ are normal vectors of the two planes, then they are perpendicular if and only if $\mathbf{v} \cdot \mathbf{w} = 0$. For example,

$$2x - y + 3z = 7 \quad \text{and} \quad 5x + 4y - 2z = 11$$

are equations of perpendicular planes since

$$(2\mathbf{i} - \mathbf{j} + 3\mathbf{k}) \cdot (5\mathbf{i} + 4\mathbf{j} - 2\mathbf{k}) = 0.$$

If two planes are not parallel, then they intersect in a line. We can find parametric equations of their line of intersection, as shown in the following example.

Example 4. Find parametric equations of the line L of intersection of the planes with equations

$$x - y + 2z = 4,$$

$$3x + y - z = 2.$$

Solution: By letting $z = 0$ in both equations and solving the resulting system for x and y, we see that $(\frac{3}{2}, -\frac{5}{2}, 0)$ is a point on L. By letting $z = 2$, we see that $(1, 1, 2)$ is another point on this line. Therefore the vector with components $(1 - \frac{3}{2}, 1 + \frac{5}{2}, 2)$, or $(-\frac{1}{2}, \frac{7}{2}, 2)$, is in the direction of L. We may, if we wish, multiply these components by 2 to obtain an integral set, $(-1, 7, 4)$, of components of a vector in the direction of L. Using $(1, 1, 2)$ as a point on L, we have by 4.23 that

$$x = 1 - t, \quad y = 1 + 7t, \quad z = 2 + 4t$$

are parametric equations of L.

EXERCISES

In each of Exercises 1–4 find an equation of the plane passing through the given point and having the given normal vector.

1. $(2, 4, -3)$, $\mathbf{i} + 3\mathbf{j} - 3\mathbf{k}$.
2. $(0, 1, 5)$, $\mathbf{i} - 7\mathbf{j}$.
3. $(1, -4, -5)$, $-3\mathbf{j} - 4\mathbf{j} + \mathbf{k}$.
4. $(-2, -7, 8)$, $\mathbf{j} + 2\mathbf{k}$.

In each of Exercises 5–8 find an equation of the plane passing through the three given points.

5. $(1, 1, 1)$, $(2, -2, 2)$, $(-1, 1, 1)$.
6. $(0, 0, 0)$, $(2, 1, 0)$, $(3, 0, 2)$.
7. $(4, 1, 2)$, $(-1, 1, 1)$, $(3, 1, -1)$.
8. $(-1, 0, 0)$, $(0, 2, 0)$, $(0, 0, 5)$.

In each of Exercises 9 and 10 find parametric equations of the lines of intersection of the planes with given equations.

9. $3x - y = 4$, $y + 2z = 5$.
10. $x + 2y + 3z = 6$, $2x - y + z = 2$.
11. Find an equation of the plane passing through the two points $(1, -1, 1)$ and $(-1, 1, 1)$ which is perpendicular to the plane with equation $2x - y + 5z = 1$.
12. Find an equation of the plane passing through the point $(4, -1, 3)$ which is perpendicular to the planes with equations $x + 2y - 3z = 3$ and $2x + y + 4z = 1$.

Appendix

1. FIELDS

Among the common number systems of mathematics are:

Z, the system of integers,
Q, the system of rational numbers,
R, the system of real numbers,
C, the system of complex numbers.

These are increasingly larger sets of numbers,

$$\mathsf{Z} \subset \mathsf{Q} \subset \mathsf{R} \subset \mathsf{C}.$$

Each of these systems is closed under the operations of addition and multiplication, which have the following properties:

A.1 $a + b = b + a, \quad ab = ba.$ (*Commutative laws*)

A.2 $a + (b + c) = (a + b) + c, \quad a(bc) = (ab)c.$ (*Associative laws*)

A.3 $(a + b)c = ac + bc, \quad c(a + b) = ca + cb.$ (*Distributive law*)

There exist numbers 0 and 1 with the following special property:

A.4 $0 + a = a + 0 = a, \quad 1 \cdot a = a \cdot 1 = a.$ (*Identity elements*)

Thus 0 is called the additive identity element and 1 the multiplicative identity element. Each number a has an opposite $-a$, called the negative of a, having the following property:

A.5 $a + (-a) = (-a) + a = 0.$ (*Additive inverse*)

The five properties above hold for all elements a, b, c in any one of the systems Z, Q, R, or C. The systems Q, R, and C also have the following additional property: each nonzero number a has a reciprocal $1/a$ such that

A.6 $$a \cdot \frac{1}{a} = \frac{1}{a} \cdot a = 1. \quad (\textit{Multiplicative inverse})$$

We are now in a position to make the following definition.

A.7. DEFINITION OF A FIELD. An algebraic system composed of a set of elements F and operations of addition and multiplication in F is called a field if and only if the operations have properties A.1–A.6.

Thus, according to this definition, the systems of rational numbers, real numbers, and complex numbers are examples of fields.

There exist fields of quite a different nature from $\mathbf{Q}$, $\mathbf{R}$, and $\mathbf{C}$. For example, for each prime number p there is a unique field having exactly p elements. This field is called the field of *integers modulo p* and is denoted by $\mathbf{Z}_p$,

$$\mathbf{Z}_p = \{0, 1, 2, \cdots, p - 1\}.$$

Addition and multiplication in $\mathbf{Z}_p$ are defined to be the same as addition and multiplication in $\mathbf{Z}$, reduced modulo p. That is, to find $a + b$ and $a \cdot b$ for $a, b \in \mathbf{Z}_p$, we first compute them in $\mathbf{Z}$ and then subtract multiples of p from $a + b$ and $a \cdot b$ until we find a remainder in $\mathbf{Z}_p$. For example, in $\mathbf{Z}$ we have $3 + 4 = 7$; therefore $3 + 4 = 7 - 5 = 2$ in $\mathbf{Z}_5$, and $3 + 4 = 7 - 7 = 0$ in $\mathbf{Z}_7$. Similarly, $3 \cdot 4 = 12$ in $\mathbf{Z}$; therefore $3 \cdot 4 = 12 - 10 = 2$ in $\mathbf{Z}_5$, and $3 \cdot 4 = 12 - 7 = 5$ in $\mathbf{Z}_7$. It is not hard to show that $\mathbf{Z}_p$ with operations of addition and multiplication so defined is a field.

Since each of the fields $\mathbf{Z}_p$, p a prime, is finite, we can give complete addition and multiplication tables for it. For example, the field $\mathbf{Z}_2 = \{0, 1\}$ has the simple tables:

+	0	1
0	0	1
1	1	0

·	0	1
0	0	0
1	0	1

The field $\mathbf{Z}_3 = \{0, 1, 2\}$ has the following addition and multiplication tables:

+	0	1	2
0	0	1	2
1	1	2	0
2	2	0	1

·	0	1	2
0	0	0	0
1	0	1	2
2	0	2	1

Starting with any field F, we can form another field $F(X)$ consisting of all rational expressions of the form

$$\frac{f(X)}{g(X)},$$

where $f(X)$ and $g(X)$ are polynomials in the symbol X, with $g(X) \neq 0$. Thus, for example,

$$\frac{3X}{X^2 - X + 1}, \quad \frac{X^5 - 3X^4 + 2X - 1}{X^2 + 5X + 3}$$

are elements of $\mathsf{Q}(X)$. Rational expressions are added and multiplied in the same way as rational numbers. Thus, for all polynomials $a(X)$, $b(X)$, $c(X)$, and $d(X)$, with $b(X) \neq 0$ and $d(X) \neq 0$, define

$$\frac{a(X)}{b(X)} + \frac{c(X)}{d(X)} = \frac{a(X)d(X) + b(X)c(X)}{b(X)d(X)}$$

$$\frac{a(X)}{b(X)} \cdot \frac{c(X)}{d(X)} = \frac{a(X)c(X)}{b(X)d(X)}.$$

The proof that $F(X)$ is a field is the same as the proof that Q is a field. The field $F(X)$ is called a *transcendental extension* of field F.

There is another fundamental way of forming fields, exemplified by

$$\mathsf{Q}[\sqrt{2}] = \{a + b\sqrt{2} \mid a, b \in \mathsf{Q}\}.$$

It is easily shown that $\mathsf{Q}[\sqrt{2}]$ is a field containing Q as a subfield. The field $\mathsf{Q}[\sqrt{2}]$ is called an *algebraic extension* of Q.

Another example of an algebraic extension of a field is the complex field

$$\mathsf{C} = \{a + bi \mid a, b \in \mathsf{R}\}, \qquad i^2 = -1,$$

which is an algebraic extension of R. A discussion of algebraic extensions of fields can be found in most textbooks on modern algebra.*

† See, for example, R. E. Johnson, *University Algebra*, Prentice-Hall, 1966.

Rational numbers and real numbers are ordered in the sense that for any two such numbers one is greater than or equal to the other. Relative to this relation of "greater than or equal to," **Q** and **R** are ordered fields as defined below.

A.8. DEFINITION OF AN ORDERED FIELD. A field F is called an ordered field if and only if it has a relation $\geq$ with the following properties:

(1) $a \geq a$ for all $a \in F$. (*Reflexive*)
(2) If $a \geq b$ and $b \geq a$, then $a = b$. (*Antisymmetric*)
(3) If $a \geq b$ and $b \geq c$, then $a \geq c$. (*Transitive*)
(4) For all $a, b \in F$, either $a \geq b$ or $b \geq a$.
(5) If $a \geq b$, then $a + c \geq b + c$ for all $c \in F$.
(6) If $a \geq b$, then $ac \geq bc$ for all $c \geq 0$.

The other order relations $>$, $\leq$, and $<$ are defined as usual. Thus $a > b$ if and only if $a \geq b$ and $a \neq b$; $a \leq b$ if and only if $b \geq a$; and $a < b$ if and only if $b > a$. The relation $>$ (and, similarly, $<$) has the following properties:

A.9 If $a > b$ and $b > c$, then $a > c$. (*Transitive*)

A.10 If $a > b$, then $a + c > b + c$ for all $c \in F$.

A.11 If $a > b$, then $ac > bc$ for all $c > 0$.

Proof of A.9: If $a > b$ and $b > c$, then $a \geq b$ and $b \geq c$ so that $a \geq c$ by A.8(3). We claim $a > c$; for if $a = c$, then $c \geq b$, $b \geq c$, and $b = c$ by A.9(2), contrary to the assumption that $b > c$.

Proof of A.10: If $a > b$, then $a + c \geq b + c$ for all $c \in F$. If $a + c = b + c$, then $a = b$ by the additive cancellation law, contrary to the fact that $a > b$. Hence $a + c > b + c$.

Proof of A.11: If $a > b$ and $c > 0$, then $ac \geq bc$ by A.8(6). If $ac = bc$, then $a = b$ by the multiplicative cancellation law (since $c \neq 0$). This is contrary to the fact that $a > b$. Hence $ac > bc$.

If we let F be an ordered field and

$$F^+ = \{a \in F \mid a > 0\}, \quad F^- = \{a \in F \mid a < 0\},$$

then we easily prove the following:

A.12 F^+ is closed under addition and multiplication.

A.13 $F^- = \{-a \mid a \in F^+\}$.

Proof of A.12: Let $a > 0$ and $b > 0$. Then $ab > 0b = 0$ by A.11. Also, $a + b > 0 + b > 0$ and $a + b > 0$ by A.10 and A.9. We conclude that if $a, b \in F^+$, then $ab, a + b \in F^+$.

Proof of A.13: If $a \in F$, $a \neq 0$, then either $a > 0$ or $a < 0$ by A.8(4). Thus either $a \in F^+$ or $a \in F^-$. If $a \neq 0$, then $-a \neq 0$ also, and either $-a \in F^+$ or $-a \in F^-$. If $a \in F^+$, then we cannot have $-a \in F^+$ also, for then $a + (-a) = 0 \in F^+$ by A.12, contrary to the fact that $b > 0$ for all $b \in F^+$. Thus if $a \in F^+$, then $-a \in F^-$. Similarly, if $b \in F^-$, then $-b \in F^+$. Since $b = -(-b)$, every $b \in F^-$ has the form $b = -a$ for some $a \in F^+$.

By our remarks above, every ordered field F is partitioned into three nonoverlapping subsets: F^+, the set of *positive elements*; F^-, the set of *negative elements;* and $\{0\}$:

$$F = F^+ \cup F^- \cup \{0\}.$$

Since $(-a)^2 = a^2$ for every nonzero $a \in F$ and either a or $-a$ is in F^+, we have by A.12 that:

A.14 $a^2 > 0$ for all nonzero $a \in F$.

In particular, $1 > 0$ since $1^2 = 1$. In turn, $1 + 1 = 2 > 0$, $1 + 2 = 3 > 0$, and so on, by the closure of F^+ under addition.

A field such as Z_p is not ordered. For if Z_p were ordered, then $1 > 0$, $2 > 0$, and so on, up to $(p - 1) + 1 > 0$, contrary to the fact that $(p - 1) + 1 = 0$.

The field C of complex numbers is also not ordered. Thus it contains an element i such that $i^2 = -1$, and if it were ordered, then both -1 and 1 would be in C^+ by A.14. However, then $0 = (-1) + 1 \in \mathsf{C}^+$ by A.12, contrary to the fact that $0 \notin \mathsf{C}^+$.

If F is an ordered field and $A \subset F$, $A \neq \emptyset$, then an element b of F is called an *upper bound* of set A if and only if $x \leq b$ for all $x \in A$. Similarly, $c \in F$ is called a *lower bound* of set A if and only if $c \leq x$ for all $x \in F$. If b is an upper bound of A, whereas no element of F smaller than b is an upper bound of A, then b is called a *least upper bound* (l.u.b.) of set A. By definition, if a set has a l.u.b., then the l.u.b. is unique. However, a set need not have a l.u.b. The *greatest lower bound* (g.l.b.) of a set is defined similarly.

An ordered field F is called *complete* if and only if every subset of F which has an upper bound has a l.u.b. It is easily demonstrated that every subset of a complete field which has a lower bound has a g.l.b. It may be proved that the field R of real numbers is uniquely characterized by the following statement.

A.15. The field R is a complete ordered field.

This characterization of R allows us to show, for example, that every $a \in \mathsf{R}^+$ has a unique nth root $\sqrt[n]{a} \in \mathsf{R}^+$ for every integer $n > 1$. Thus it can be shown that

$$\sqrt[n]{a} = \text{l.u.b. } \{x \in \mathsf{R}^+ \mid x^n \leq a\}.$$

The field C of complex numbers is given by

$$\mathsf{C} = \{a + bi \mid a, b \in \mathsf{R}\}, \text{ where } i^2 = -1.$$

Actually, C is a vector space over R,

$$\mathsf{C} = \mathsf{R}1 + \mathsf{R}i.$$

Since $\mathsf{R}1 \cap \mathsf{R}i = \{0\}$, C is a *two-dimensional vector space* over R. Of course, it is also a vector algebra because of its operation of multiplication defined by

$$(a + bi)(c + di) = (ac - bd) + (ad + bc)i.$$

As we pointed out in Chapter Four, C is isomorphic to the vector algebra V_2.

2. COORDINATE SYSTEMS

An interesting property of R is that it can be used as a set of coordinates for the points on a line L. When this is done in the usual way, each point on L is assigned a unique real number as its coordinate and each real number is the coordinate of a unique point on L. Furthermore, the order in R is preserved on L; i.e., if point B is between points A and C on L, then the coordinate of B is between the coordinates of A and C. An arrowhead is placed on L to indicate the direction of increasing coordinates, as shown in Fig. A.1.

We shall call a line L having R as a coordinate system a *coordinate line* or a *coordinate axis*. The point on L with coordinate 0 is called the *origin*.

The numbers are assigned in a regular way on a coordinate line so that distances may be easily computed as follows.

A.16. DISTANCE FORMULA ON A LINE. If points A and B on a coordinate line have respective coordinates a and b, then the distance $d(A, B)$ between A and B is given by

$$d(A, B) = |b - a|.$$

At times it is convenient to use directed distances on a coordinate line L. If points A and B on L have respective coordinates a and b, then the *directed distance* from A to B is defined to be $b - a$. Thus, by definition, the directed distance from A to B is simply $d(A, B)$ if the direction from A to B is the direction of L, zero if $A = B$, and $-d(A, B)$ if the direction from A to B is opposite to the direction of L.

The set R_2 of all ordered pairs of real numbers can be used as a set of coordinates for the points in a Euclidean plane E_2. This is usually done as shown in Fig. A.2. Thus two perpendicular coordinate axes are chosen in E_2 so that they intersect at their origins. One of the coordinate axes in labeled the *x-axis* and the other the *y-axis*. Each point P in E_2 has unique coordinates (a, b) in R_2, where the coordinate of the foot of the perpendicular drawn from P to the x-axis is a and from P to the y-axis is b. Also, each ordered pair (a, b) in R_2 are the coordinates of a unique point in E_2 chosen in the obvious way. If point P in E_2 has coordinate (a, b) in R_2, then we call a the *x-coordinate* and b the *y-coordinate* of P. We shall call a plane having R_2 as a set of coordinates in the

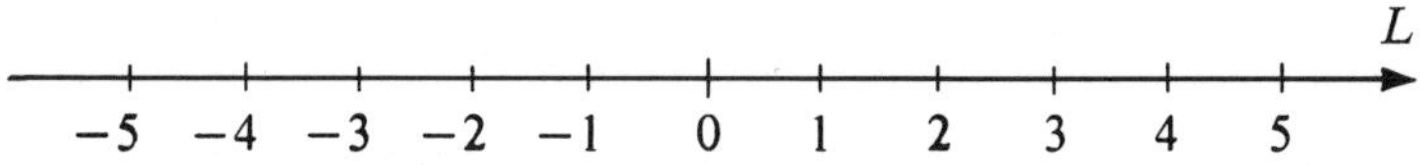

Figure A.1

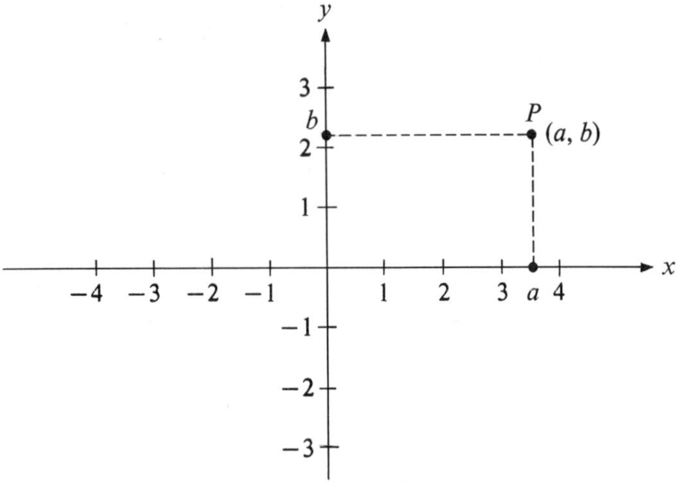

Figure A.2

manner described above a *rectangular coordinate plane* or a *Cartesian plane*.

If the x-axis and the y-axis in a Cartesian plane have the same scale, then we can find the distance between any two points in the plane as follows.

A.17. DISTANCE FORMULA IN A PLANE. If points A and B in a coordinate plane have respective coordinates (a_1, a_2) and (b_1, b_2), then the distance $d(A, B)$ between A and B is given by

$$d(A, B) = \sqrt{(a_1 - b_1)^2 + (a_2 - b_2)^2}.$$

We shall not give the proof of A.17. It follows readily from the Pythagorean Theorem and A.16.

The set R_3 of all ordered triplets of real numbers can be used as a set of coordinates for the points in Euclidean space E_3. This is usually accomplished by selecting three mutually perpendicular coordinate axes intersecting at their origins. Let us label these axes the x-axis, the y-axis, and the z-axis. Each point P in E_3 has unique coordinates (a, b, c) in R_3, where the coordinate of the foot of the perpendicular drawn from P to the x-axis is a, from P to the y-axis is b, and from P to the z-axis is c (Fig. A.3). Also, each ordered triplet (a, b, c) in R_3 are the coordinates of a unique point in E_3. If P has coordinates (a, b, c), then we call a the *x-coordinate*, b the *y-coordinate*, and c the *z-coordinate* of P. We shall call E_3 *Cartesian three-space* if coordinates are assigned to the points of E_3 in the manner described above.

If the coordinate axes in a Cartesian three-space have the same scale, then the distance between two points in E_3 can be found as follows.

A.18. DISTANCE FORMULA IN SPACE. If points A and B in coordinate three-space have respective coordinates (a_1, a_2, a_3) and (b_1, b_2, b_3), then the distance $d(A, B)$ between A and B is given by

$$d(A, B) = \sqrt{(a_1 - b_1)^2 + (a_2 - b_2)^2 + (a_3 - b_3)^2}.$$

The proof of A.18 follows easily from the Pythagorean Theorem and A.17.

3. UNITARY SPACES

The complex number field C is often used in applications of mathematics to physics and related sciences. In some applications vector spaces are used which have complex numbers instead of real numbers for scalars. So let us consider vector spaces having C as a field of scalars.

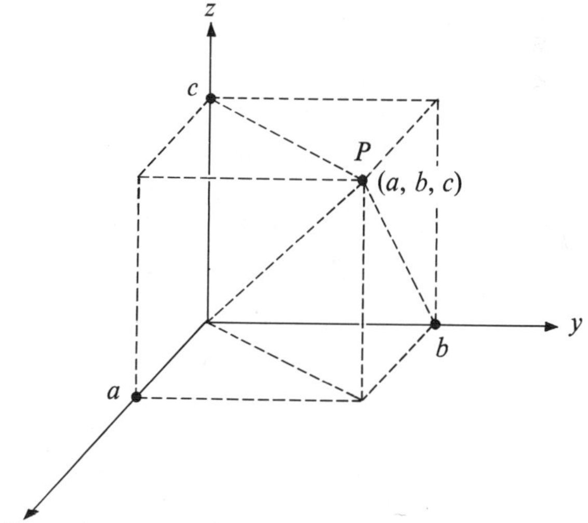

Figure A.3

Let V be a vector space having C as a field of scalars. All the results of Chapters One and Two hold equally well for a vector space over any field. Thus we call a set of nonzero vectors $\{\mathbf{x}_1, \mathbf{x}_2, \cdots, \mathbf{x}_n\}$ of V a basis if they span V(i.e., each $\mathbf{x} \in V$ has the form $\mathbf{x} = a_1\mathbf{x}_1 + a_2\mathbf{x}_2 + \cdots + a_n\mathbf{x}_n$ for some $a_1, a_2, \cdots, a_n \in \mathsf{C}$) and are linearly independent (i.e., $\mathsf{C}\mathbf{x}_i \cap (\mathsf{C}\mathbf{x}_1 + \cdots + \mathsf{C}\mathbf{x}_{i-1} + \mathsf{C}\mathbf{x}_{i+1} + \cdots + \mathsf{C}\mathbf{x}_n) = \{\mathbf{0}\}$, $i = 1, 2, \cdots, n$). If V has a basis consisting of n vectors, then n is called the dimension of V as usual.

Since $\mathsf{R} \subset \mathsf{C}$, each vector space V having C as a field of scalars also has R, a subfield of C, as a field of scalars. If V has a basis $\{\mathbf{x}_1, \mathbf{x}_2, \cdots, \mathbf{x}_n\}$ when considered as a vector space over C, then it has basis $B = \{\mathbf{x}_1, \mathbf{x}_2, \cdots, \mathbf{x}_n, i\mathbf{x}_1, i\mathbf{x}_2, \cdots, i\mathbf{x}_n\}$ when considered as a vector space over R. Thus each $\mathbf{x} \in V$ has the form $\mathbf{x} = c_1\mathbf{x}_1 + c_2\mathbf{x}_2 + \cdots + c_n\mathbf{x}_n$ for some $c_1, c_2, \cdots, c_n \in \mathsf{C}$. Now $c_1 = a_1 + ib_1$, $c_2 = a_2 + ib_2$, $\cdots$, $c_n = a_n + ib_n$ for some $a_1, a_2, \cdots, a_n, b_1, b_2, \cdots, b_n \in \mathsf{R}$. Hence

$$\mathbf{x} = a_1\mathbf{x}_1 + a_2\mathbf{x}_2 + \cdots + a_n\mathbf{x}_n + b_1i\mathbf{x}_1 + b_2i\mathbf{x}_2 + \cdots + b_ni\mathbf{x}_n;$$

i.e., B is a set of generators of V over R. Clearly $\mathbf{x} = \mathbf{0}$ above if and only if $a_1 + ib_1 = 0$, $a_2 + ib_2 = 0$, $\cdots$, $a_n + ib_n = 0$, i.e., if and only if $a_1 = a_2 = \cdots = a_n = 0$, $b_1 = b_2 = \cdots = b_n = 0$. Therefore B is a basis of V. Consequently, a vector space V of dimension n over C is of dimension $2n$ over the subfield R of C.

For each positive integer n, let C_n be the set of all n-tuples with coordinates from C. It may be shown, just as it was for R_n in Chapter One, that C_n is a vector space having C as a field of scalars. Again, $\{\mathbf{u}_1, \mathbf{u}_2, \cdots, \mathbf{u}_n\}$ is a basis of C_n where the $\mathbf{u}_i$'s are as defined on page 19. Every n-dimensional vector space over C is isomorphic to C_n.

A vector space V having C as its field of scalars is called an *inner product space* if and only if it has an inner product satisfying 3.3. Thus associated with each pair $\mathbf{x}, \mathbf{y}$ of vectors in V is their inner product $\mathbf{x}\cdot\mathbf{y}$ in C having the following properties:

(1) $(\mathbf{x} + \mathbf{y})\cdot\mathbf{z} = \mathbf{x}\cdot\mathbf{z} + \mathbf{y}\cdot\mathbf{z}$, $\mathbf{z}\cdot(\mathbf{x} + \mathbf{y}) = \mathbf{z}\cdot\mathbf{x} + \mathbf{z}\cdot\mathbf{y}$ for all $\mathbf{x}, \mathbf{y}, \mathbf{z} \in V$.

(2) $(a\mathbf{x})\cdot\mathbf{y} = a(\mathbf{x}\cdot\mathbf{y})$ for all $\mathbf{x}, \mathbf{y} \in V$, $a \in \mathsf{C}$.

(3) $\mathbf{x}\cdot\mathbf{x}$ is a real number for all $\mathbf{x} \in V$, $\mathbf{x}\cdot\mathbf{x} \geq 0$ with $\mathbf{x}\cdot\mathbf{x} = 0$ if and only if $\mathbf{x} = \mathbf{0}$.

Although $\mathbf{x}\cdot\mathbf{y}$ is not necessarily a real number, $\mathbf{x}\cdot\mathbf{x}$ is a real number according to (3) above.

A.19. DEFINITION OF A UNITARY SPACE. An inner product space V over C is called a *unitary space* if and only if

$$\mathbf{x}\cdot\mathbf{y} = \overline{\mathbf{y}\cdot\mathbf{x}} \text{ for all } \mathbf{x}, \mathbf{y} \in V.$$

In this definition we use the notation $\bar{c}$ for the conjugate of the complex number c. Thus if $c = a + bi$, where $a, b \in \mathsf{R}$, then $\bar{c} = a - bi$. It is easily verified that

$$\overline{c + d} = \bar{c} + \bar{d}, \quad \overline{cd} = \bar{c}\bar{d} \text{ for all } c, d \in \mathsf{C}.$$

The length of a vector $\mathbf{x} \in V$ is defined as in 3.6:

$$|\mathbf{x}| = \sqrt{\mathbf{x}\cdot\mathbf{x}} \text{ for all } \mathbf{x} \in V.$$

Since $\mathbf{x}\cdot\mathbf{x}$ is a positive real number if $\mathbf{x} \neq \mathbf{0}$, each nonzero vector $\mathbf{x} \in V$ has a positive length. Of course, $|\mathbf{0}| = 0$.

Each complex number c has an absolute value defined by $|c| = \sqrt{c\cdot\bar{c}}$. If $c = a + bi$, where $a, b \in \mathsf{R}$, then $|c| = \sqrt{a^2 + b^2}$. Thus $|c|$ is a real number, $|0| = 0$, and $|c| > 0$ if $c \neq 0$.

In a unitary space V we can compute $\mathbf{x}\cdot(c\mathbf{y})$ for any $\mathbf{x}, \mathbf{y} \in V$, $c \in \mathsf{C}$ as follows:

$$\mathbf{x}\cdot(c\mathbf{y}) = \overline{(c\mathbf{y})\cdot\mathbf{x}} = \overline{c(\mathbf{y}\cdot\mathbf{x})} = \bar{c}\,\overline{(\mathbf{y}\cdot\mathbf{x})} = \bar{c}(\mathbf{x}\cdot\mathbf{y}).$$

That is:

A.20 $$\mathbf{x}\cdot(c\mathbf{y}) = \bar{c}(\mathbf{x}\cdot\mathbf{y}) \text{ for all } \mathbf{x}, \mathbf{y} \in V, c \in \mathsf{C}.$$

Using A.20, we have the following analogue of 3.8 for a unitary space V:

A.21 $$\left(\sum_{i=1}^{n} a_i\mathbf{x}_i\right)\cdot\left(\sum_{j=1}^{m} b_j\mathbf{y}_j\right) = \sum_{i=1}^{n}\sum_{j=1}^{m} a_i\bar{b}_j(\mathbf{x}_i\cdot\mathbf{y}_j).$$

In particular, we have

$$|c\mathbf{x}| = \sqrt{(c\mathbf{x})\cdot(c\mathbf{x})} = \sqrt{c\bar{c}(\mathbf{x}\cdot\mathbf{x})} = \sqrt{c\bar{c}}\,\sqrt{\mathbf{x}\cdot\mathbf{x}}$$

so that

A.22 $$|c\mathbf{x}| = |c|\,|\mathbf{x}| \text{ for all } \mathbf{x} \in V, c \in \mathsf{C}.$$

Cauchy's inequality (3.9) holds for a unitary space V as well as for a Euclidean space.

A.23 $$|\mathbf{x}\cdot\mathbf{y}| \leq |\mathbf{x}|\,|\mathbf{y}| \text{ for all } \mathbf{x}, \mathbf{y} \in V.$$

Proof: As in the proof of 3.9, let $a = \mathbf{u}\cdot\mathbf{u} \neq 0$, $b = \mathbf{u}\cdot\mathbf{v}$, and $\mathbf{w} = a\mathbf{v} - \bar{b}\mathbf{u}$ Then $a \in \mathsf{R}$ and

$$\begin{aligned}\mathbf{w}\cdot\mathbf{w} &= a^2(\mathbf{v}\cdot\mathbf{v}) - ab(\mathbf{v}\cdot\mathbf{u}) - a\bar{b}(\mathbf{u}\cdot\mathbf{v}) + b\bar{b}(\mathbf{u}\cdot\mathbf{u})\\ &= a^2(\mathbf{v}\cdot\mathbf{v}) - ab\bar{b} - a\bar{b}b + ab\bar{b}\\ &= a[a(\mathbf{v}\cdot\mathbf{v}) - b\bar{b}].\end{aligned}$$

Since $\mathbf{w}\cdot\mathbf{w} \geq 0$, $a > 0$, and $b\bar{b} = |\mathbf{u}\cdot\mathbf{v}|$, we have

$$a(\mathbf{v}\cdot\mathbf{v}) - b\bar{b} \geq 0.$$

This proves A.23.

The reader may easily prove the following triangle inequality by multiplying out $(\mathbf{x} + \mathbf{y})\cdot(\mathbf{x} + \mathbf{y})$ and by using Cauchy's inequality and the fact that $a + \bar{a} \leq 2\sqrt{a\bar{a}}$ for every $a \in \mathsf{C}$ (letting $a = \mathbf{x}\cdot\mathbf{y}$).

A.24 $$|\mathbf{x} + \mathbf{y}| \leq |\mathbf{x}| + |\mathbf{y}|.$$

We shall not go into the details, but it may be proved that every finite-dimensional unitary space has a normal orthogonal basis.

The vector space C_n described above has a dot product defined as follows:

A.25 $$(a_1, a_2, \cdots, a_n)\cdot(b_1, b_2, \cdots, b_n) = \sum_{i=1}^{n} a_i\bar{b}_i.$$

The reader should have no trouble showing that the dot product is an inner product and that C_n is actually a unitary space.

4. HISTORICAL NOTE

The use of vectors to represent forces dates back at least to the Dutch physicist Simon Steven. He used the so-called "triangle of forces" in his treatise *Statics and Hydrostatics*, published in 1586. In that book he added vectors as we do in V_3 to obtain the resultant of forces in space.

However, because he did not use the cross product operation, he was working with a vector space and not a vector algebra.

The cross product operation in V_3 was discovered by the Irish mathematician, physicist, and astronomer Sir William Rowan Hamilton in the 1840s as a by-product of his work on quaternions. In the preface of his book *Lectures on Quaternions* (1853), Hamilton tells of the search for a three-dimensional vector algebra which he began in 1834 and worked on unsuccessfully for several years. He was seeking a product operation in V_3 which together with the usual operation of addition would make V_3 into a field.

He was unable to find such a product operation in V_3, which we now know had to be the case. For it may be proved that no such product exists in V_3. As often happens, however, his search led him to at least as important a discovery of a different nature. He discovered a four-dimensional vector algebra H, which he called the *algebra of quaternions*. If we think of H as R_4, then a basis of H is $\{\mathbf{u}_1, \mathbf{u}_2, \mathbf{u}_3, \mathbf{u}_4\}$ where, as usual,

$$\mathbf{u}_1 = (1,0,0,0), \quad \mathbf{u}_2 = (0,1,0,0), \quad \mathbf{u}_3 = (0,0,1,0), \quad \mathbf{u}_4 = (0,0,0,1).$$

The unit quaternions above are multiplied according to the table below. To find $\mathbf{u}_i \times \mathbf{u}_j$ by this table, we look in the column below $\times$ for $\mathbf{u}_i$ and in the row to the right of $\times$ for $\mathbf{u}_j$. Then $\mathbf{u}_i \times \mathbf{u}_j$ is the entry in the table to the right of $\mathbf{u}_i$ and directly below $\mathbf{u}_j$. For example,

$$\mathbf{u}_2 \times \mathbf{u}_3 = \mathbf{u}_4, \quad \mathbf{u}_3 \times \mathbf{u}_2 = -\mathbf{u}_4, \quad \mathbf{u}_4 \times \mathbf{u}_3 = -\mathbf{u}_2.$$

$\times$	$\mathbf{u}_1$	$\mathbf{u}_2$	$\mathbf{u}_3$	$\mathbf{u}_4$
$\mathbf{u}_1$	$\mathbf{u}_1$	$\mathbf{u}_2$	$\mathbf{u}_3$	$\mathbf{u}_4$
$\mathbf{u}_2$	$\mathbf{u}_2$	$-\mathbf{u}_1$	$\mathbf{u}_4$	$-\mathbf{u}_3$
$\mathbf{u}_3$	$\mathbf{u}_3$	$-\mathbf{u}_4$	$-\mathbf{u}_1$	$\mathbf{u}_2$
$\mathbf{u}_4$	$\mathbf{u}_4$	$\mathbf{u}_3$	$-\mathbf{u}_2$	$-\mathbf{u}_1$

Having defined multiplication for a basis of H, we can then define multiplication in H itself in a natural way. Thus for all (a_1, a_2, a_3, a_4), $(b_1, b_2, b_3, b_4) \in H$ we have

$$(a_1, a_2, a_3, a_4) = \sum_{i=1}^{4} a_i\mathbf{u}_i,$$

$$(b_1, b_2, b_3, b_4) = \sum_{j=1}^{4} b_j\mathbf{u}_j,$$

and we define

A.26 $$\left(\sum_{i=1}^{4} a_i\mathbf{u}_i\right) \times \left(\sum_{j=1}^{4} b_j\mathbf{u}_j\right) = \sum_{i=1}^{4}\sum_{j=1}^{4} a_ib_j(\mathbf{u}_i \times \mathbf{u}_j).$$

That is, we multiply each term of the first sum by each term of the second, which yields 16 terms ont he right side of equation A.26.

Example 1. Find the product $\mathbf{x} \times \mathbf{y}$, where $\mathbf{x} = (0, 1, -2, 2)$ and $\mathbf{y} = (1, -3, 4, 0)$.

Solution: We have

$$\mathbf{x} = \mathbf{u}_2 - 2\mathbf{u}_3 + 2\mathbf{u}_4, \quad \mathbf{y} = \mathbf{u}_1 - 3\mathbf{u}_2 + 4\mathbf{u}_3.$$

Hence

$$\begin{aligned}\mathbf{x} \times \mathbf{y} &= (\mathbf{u}_2 - 2\mathbf{u}_3 + 2\mathbf{u}_4) \times (\mathbf{u}_1 - 3\mathbf{u}_2 + 4\mathbf{u}_3)\\ &= \mathbf{u}_2 \times \mathbf{u}_1 - 3(\mathbf{u}_2 \times \mathbf{u}_2) + 4(\mathbf{u}_2 \times \mathbf{u}_3) - 2(\mathbf{u}_3 \times \mathbf{u}_1)\\ &\quad + 6(\mathbf{u}_3 \times \mathbf{u}_2)\\ &\quad - 8(\mathbf{u}_3 \times \mathbf{u}_3) + 2(\mathbf{u}_4 \times \mathbf{u}_1) - 6(\mathbf{u}_4 \times \mathbf{u}_2) + 8(\mathbf{u}_4 \times \mathbf{u}_3).\end{aligned}$$

Using the multiplication table above, we get

$$\begin{aligned}\mathbf{x} \times \mathbf{y} &= \mathbf{u}_2 + 3\mathbf{u}_1 + 4\mathbf{u}_4 - 2\mathbf{u}_3 - 6\mathbf{u}_4 + 8\mathbf{u}_1 + 2\mathbf{u}_4 - 6\mathbf{u}_3 - 8\mathbf{u}_2\\ &= 11\mathbf{u}_1 - 7\mathbf{u}_2 - 8\mathbf{u}_3\\ &= (11, -7, -8, 0).\end{aligned}$$

If we simplify the right side of equation A.26 the way we did the example above, then we get

A.27 $$\begin{aligned}\left(\sum_{i=1}^{4} a_i\mathbf{u}_i\right) \times \left(\sum_{j=1}^{4} b_j\mathbf{u}_j\right) &= (a_1b_1 - a_2b_2 - a_3b_3 - a_4b_4)\mathbf{u}_1\\ &\quad + (a_1b_2 + a_2b_1 + a_3b_4 - a_4b_3)\mathbf{u}_2\\ &\quad + (a_1b_3 + a_3b_1 + a_4b_2 - a_2b_4)\mathbf{u}_3\\ &\quad + (a_1b_4 + a_4b_1 + a_2b_3 - a_3b_2)\mathbf{u}_4.\end{aligned}$$

This equation defines the product of every pair of quaternions.

We shall not carry through the proof, but it may be shown that Hamilton's quaternion algebra H has properties A.1–A.6 of a field, with the exception of the multiplicative part of A.1. Thus H is a *non-commutative field.* That multiplication is not commutative is evident from the table of products of the unit vectors: for example, $\mathbf{u}_2 \times \mathbf{u}_3 = \mathbf{u}_4$, whereas $\mathbf{u}_3 \times \mathbf{u}_2 = -\mathbf{u}_4$. It may be shown that multiplication in H is anticommutative:

A.28 $$\mathbf{x} \times \mathbf{y} = -\mathbf{y} \times \mathbf{x} \text{ for all } \mathbf{x}, \mathbf{y} \in H.$$

As Hamilton points out in his preface, it is quite easy to get a three-dimensional vector algebra from H. We need only consider

$$\mathbf{i} = (0, 1, 0, 0), \quad \mathbf{j} = (0, 0, 1, 0), \quad \mathbf{k} = (0, 0, 0, 1)$$

and then multiply vectors in V_3 according to A.27, taking care to omit the first term (the one containing $\mathbf{u}_1$). Thus

$$\begin{aligned}(a_2\mathbf{i} + a_3\mathbf{j} + a_4\mathbf{k}) \times (b_2\mathbf{i} + b_3\mathbf{j} + b_4\mathbf{k}) = &(a_3b_4 - a_4b_3)\mathbf{i} \\ &+ (a_4b_2 - a_2b_4)\mathbf{j} \\ &+ (a_2b_3 - a_3b_2)\mathbf{k}\end{aligned}$$

according to A.27 (letting $a_1 = 0$, $b_1 = 0$, and omitting the first term). We see immediately that this is the same as 4.12.

Although Hamilton showed how to define multiplication in V_3, he never used the algebra V_3 in his work. It remained for the physicists J. Willard Gibbs and Oliver Heaviside to exploit this algebra in the 1880s and show its wide applicability to physics and other sciences.

Index

Basic, 27

Cauchy's inequality, 54, 106
Centroid of a triangle, 28
of a tetrahedron, 35
Components, 42, 44
Cross product, 72

Dependence, 23
Dimension, 32
Direction cosines, 86
Dot product, 51

Euclidean space, 53

Field, 96
Free vector, 7

Geometric vector, 6
Generator, 38

Homomorphism, 39

Independence, 23
Inner product, 53
Inner product space, 53, 104
Intersection of subspaces, 4
Isomorphism, 40

Kernel, 50

Length of a vector, 54
Linear combination, 6
Linearly dependent, 26
Linearly independent, 26

Lines in space, 80

Mapping, 38
1-1 Mapping, 40

n-tuple, 18
Normal vector, 54
of a plane, 90
Normal orthogonal basis, 64

Ordered field, 98
Orthogonal, 64

Parametric equations of a line, 81
Planes, 88
Position vector, 42
Proper subspace, 4

Quaternions, 107

Replacement property, 30

Scalar, 2
Span, 6
Subspace, 4
Sum of subspaces, 5
Symmetric form of line equation, 82

Unit vector, 54
Unitary space, 105

Vector, 2
Vector algebra, 67
Vector space, 1